D1627272

INTERSCIENCE TRACTS ON PHYSICS AND ASTRONOMY

Edited by R. E. MARSHAK

University of Rochester

1. D. J. Hughes
   NEUTRON OPTICS
2. M. S. Livingston
   HIGH-ENERGY ACCELERATORS
3. L. Spitzer, Jr.
   PHYSICS OF FULLY IONIZED GASES, second edition
4. T. G. Cowling
   MAGNETOHYDRODYNAMICS
5. D. ter Haar
   INTRODUCTION TO THE PHYSICS OF MANY-BODY SYSTEMS
6. E. K. Öpik
   PHYSICS OF METEOR FLIGHT IN THE ATMOSPHERE
7. K. Mendelssohn
   CRYOPHYSICS
8. J. L. Delcroix
   INTRODUCTION TO THE THEORY OF IONIZED GASES
9. T. E. Sterne
   AN INTRODUCTION TO CELESTIAL MECHANICS
10. J. Weber
    GENERAL RELATIVITY AND GRAVITATIONAL WAVES
11. R. E. Marshak and E. C. G. Sudarshan
    INTRODUCTION TO ELEMENTARY PARTICLE PHYSICS
12. J. L. Olsen
    ELECTRON TRANSPORT IN METALS
13. M. Françon
    MODERN APPLICATIONS OF PHYSICAL OPTICS
14. P. B. Jones
    THE OPTICAL MODEL IN NUCLEAR AND PARTICLE PHYSICS
15. R. K. Adair and E. C. Fowler
    STRANGE PARTICLES
16. R. Wilson
    THE NUCLEON-NUCLEON INTERACTION: EXPERIMENTAL AND PHENOMENOLOGICAL ASPECTS
17. J. F. Denisse and J. L. Delcroix
    PLASMA WAVES

18. **W. F. Brown, Jr.**
     MICROMAGNETICS
19. **A. Rose**
     *CONCEPTS IN PHOTOCONDUCTIVITY AND ALLIED
     PROBLEMS*
20. **A. Guinier and D. L. Dexter**
     X-RAY STUDIES OF MATERIALS
21. **T. G. Northrup**
     THE ADIABATIC MOTION OF CHARGED PARTICLES
22. **G. Barton**
     INTRODUCTION TO ADVANCED FIELD THEORY
23. **C. D. Jeffries**
     DYNAMIC NUCLEAR ORIENTATION
24. **G. B. Benedek**
     MAGNETIC RESONANCE AT HIGH PRESSURE

Additional volumes in preparation

PLASMA WAVES

J. F. DENISSE

*Observatoire de Paris,
Paris, France*

and

J. L. DELCROIX

*Faculté des Sciences de Paris,
Paris, France*

TRANSLATED FROM THE FRENCH BY

Marcel Weinrich and David J. BenDaniel

*General Electric Research Laboratory,
Schenectady, New York*

INTERSCIENCE PUBLISHERS 1963

a division of John Wiley & Sons, New York · London · Sydney

Introduction

The topic of wave propagation in plasmas has been the subject of much literature. Most of its aspects have been treated in a detailed manner, but in different areas of approximation.

In this book we undertook the task of presenting an integrated study of waves in plasmas, looking to describe the types of existing waves in as general and as systematic a frame as possible. To achieve this goal, while working to keep the book within a reasonable size, it was necessary to neglect in some measure, or even completely, certain important problems (absorption phenomena, nonlinear phenomena, microscopic representation of a plasma, experiments, etc.), and on the other hand to treat some problems which might be judged of a somewhat academic interest.

We hope that, in spite of these omissions and shortcomings, this book can be of service to researchers and students who, be they physicists, astrophysicists, or geophysicists, are interested in the peculiar behavior of plasmas.

Some new results are presented in this book, notably in Chapters 5, 6, and 8; it appeared to us important to publish them here for the sake of comprehension of this topic as a whole. However, as they have not been previously submitted to the test of prior publication, they will, presumably, be the object of certain criticisms which we will receive with gratitude.

We are indeed very pleased to express our thanks to D. Quemada, who has helped us in the editing of Appendix 1, to P. Feautriev, who prepared a program of general solutions to the eigenvalue equation, and especially to J. Pihan, who has generously devoted his time to the numerical computations and to the plotting of the dispersion curves which illustrate this book.

J. F. DENISSE

J. L. DELCROIX

Translators' Preface

We have endeavored to preserve the thoughts, order of presentation, and emphasis of the French original of this text. Whenever compromises or modifications were made to obtain clarity in the translation, it is our hope that these choices will be of benefit to the reader. We have not attempted to verify all the extensive algebraic and numerical computations contained herein. A number of corrections, of the nature of errata, were made.

We wish to express our gratitude to Dr. H. Hurwitz, Jr., for his support.

DAVID BENDANIEL

MARCEL WEINRICH

Schenectady, N. Y.
July 1963

Contents

1. General Equations 1

   1.1   Macroscopic Variables Which Characterize a Plasma . . . 1
   1.2   Interaction Between Electromagnetic Field and Particles . . 3

2. Dispersion Relation for Plane Waves 7

   2.1   Properties of Monochromatic Plane Waves 7
   2.2   The General Dispersion Equation 10
   2.3   Singularities in the Dispersion Equation 15
        a. Case where B_0 is zero. Linearly polarized transverse
           waves; longitudinal waves 15
        b. Case where B_0 is longitudinal; existence of two distinct
           transverse waves 15
        c. B_0 arbitrary. Coupling between transverse and longi-
           tudinal waves 16
   2.4   General Notation 17

3. Transverse Electromagnetic Waves ($B_T = 0$) 19

   3.1   General Equations—Ordinary and Extraordinary Waves . . 19
        a. Dispersion relation 19
        b. Polarization of the two waves 21
        c. Dispersion curves 22
   3.2   High Frequency Region 24
        a. No magnetic field 24
        b. Magnetic field present 25
   3.3   Low Frequency Region—Alfvén Waves 25
        a. Limits of the index of refraction 25
        b. Discussion. Dense plasma; magnetodynamic approxi-
           mation 26
        c. Linearly polarized waves 26

4. Longitudinal Waves ($B_T = 0$) 32

   4.1   General Relations 32
        a. Dispersion equation and curve 32
        b. Ratio of electron-to-ion speeds 35

4.2   Electron Waves: Plasma Electron Oscillations   36
       a. Ion motion   36
       b. Dispersion relation   37
       c. Phase and group velocities   39
       d. Distinction between sound waves and plasma oscillations   40
       e. Microscopic analysis of plasma oscillations   41
4.3   Ion Waves: Ion Oscillations in a Plasma and Pseudosonic
       Waves   43
       a. Oscillation of ions in a plasma   43
       b. Conditions for the existence of ion oscillations in a plasma   44
       c. Pseudosonic waves   46

5. Classification of Waves and Plasmas   49

5.1   Transfer of Energy in a Wave   49
       a. The various forms of the energy   49
       b. Equation for electromagnetic energy transfer   50
       c. Equation for mechanical energy transfer   50
5.2   The Relation of Various Forms of Energy   52
5.3   Some Comments about Transverse and Longitudinal Waves .   54
5.4   Classification of Plasmas   55
5.5   Numerical Values for Five Typical Cases   59

6. The Four Modes of Propagation in the General Case ($B_T = 0$)   60

6.1   General Dispersion Relation   60
       a. Existence and orthogonality of four modes   60
       b. Wave polarization   62
       c. Expansion of the determinant (Eq. 2.2)   64
6.2   Properties of the Dispersion Curve   65
       a. General picture and special cases   65
       b. High frequency waves; nomenclature for the four modes   66
       c. Resonance frequencies   68
       d. Critical frequencies   68
       e. Limits of the speed of low frequency waves; magneto-
          dynamic waves (horizontal asymptotes of the dispersion
          curve)   69
       f. Oblique asymptotes   69
6.3   Double Points of the Dispersion Curve; General Definition
       of the Four Modes   70
6.4   Quasi-longitudinal Propagation   72
       a. Behavior of the curve in the neighborhood of a coupling
          point   72

b. General behavior of curves C_T and C_L. Points of coupling   73
c. Dispersion curves for five typical plasmas   76

7. Transverse Propagation ($B_L = 0$)   78

7.1 Dispersion Equation and Curve   78
7.2 Wave Polarization   82

8. Propagation in Cold Plasmas   84

8.1 Dispersion Equation and Curve   85
8.2 Vertical Asymptotes: Resonance Frequencies   85
     a. General equation   85
     b. Longitudinal propagation   87
     c. Transverse propagation   87
     d. Oblique propagation   88
8.3 Horizontal Asymptotes: Magnetodynamic Waves   89
8.4 Identification of the Modes   89
8.5 Transverse Propagation   93
8.6 High Frequency Approximation Appleton-Hartree Equation   93
8.7 Polarization of the Waves   96
     a. General properties of transverse polarization   96
     b. High frequency case Appleton-Hartree approximation   97

9. Magnetodynamic Waves   99

9.1 Speeds of Propagation   99
     a. General equations; oblique Alfvén wave and magneto-
        acoustic waves   99
     b. Propagation speed as a function of the propagation angle   101
9.2 Polarization of Magnetodynamic Waves   103
     a. Polarization of the oblique Alfvén wave   104
     b. Polarization of the accelerated and retarded magneto-
        acoustic waves   106
     c. Energies   109

Appendix 1. The Conductivity Tensor   113

A1.1 General Equations   113
A1.2 Case $\nu = 0$ 114
A1.3 Case $\nu \neq 0$ 115

**Appendix 2. The Dispersion Equation as An Eigenvalue Equa-
tion ($\nu = \nu_{en} = \nu_{in} = 0$)**   116

Appendix 3. Computation and Discussion of the General Dispersion Equations 122

A3.1 Expansion of the Determinant in Table 2.2 122
A3.2 Equation in y 123
A3.3 Equation in $u = y - 1$ 123
A3.4 Equation in x 124
A3.5 Horizontal Asymptotes of the Dispersion Curve 126
A3.6 Oblique Asymptote of the Dispersion Curve 127
A3.7 Solutions Restricted to the Neighborhood of the y Axis . . 128

Appendix 4. Polarization of the Modes 129

Appendix 5. Propagation in Cold Plasmas 132

A5.1 Equation in u 132
A5.2 Vertical Asymptotes 133
A5.3 Transverse Propagation 136
A5.4 High Frequency Approximation (Appleton-Hartree Equation) 137

References 139

Index 141

CHAPTER 1

General Equations

The CGS electromagnetic system is used in this book.

1.1 Macroscopic Variables Which Characterize a Plasma

A uniform and unbounded plasma in equilibrium in a magnetic field can be characterized, from the macroscopic point of view, by the following variables which have a simple physical meaning [1, 2].

1. The average density of electrons and ions. We shall designate by $\bar{n}_e$ the average density of electrons of charge q_e and of mass m_e, $\bar{n}_i$ the average density of ions which we shall assume to be of a single species, of charge $q_i = - Zq_e$ and having a mass m_i. Note that q_e is negative. We assume that the unperturbed plasma is neutral, so that we have

$$\bar{n}_e q_e + \bar{n}_i q_i = 0 \qquad (1)$$

The plasma can also contain neutral molecules.

2. The average velocity of the ions and electrons. Since the plasma is in equilibrium, the average velocities will be zero.

$$\bar{\boldsymbol{v}}_e = \bar{\boldsymbol{v}}_i = 0 \qquad (2)$$

3. The kinetic pressure tensors. The thermal motion of the two species of particles should be represented by two kinetic pressure tensors $\boldsymbol{\Psi}_e$ and $\boldsymbol{\Psi}_i$. We shall assume in this book that $\boldsymbol{\Psi}_e$ and $\boldsymbol{\Psi}_i$ can be reduced to two scalar isotropic pressures $\bar{p}_e$ and $\bar{p}_i$, which can be expressed as a function of the temperatures T_e and T_i of the electrons and the ions by the formulas

$$\bar{p}_e = \bar{n}_e K T_e \tag{3}$$

$$\bar{p}_i = \bar{n}_i K T_i \tag{4}$$

The temperatures T_e and T_i are equal when the gases are in thermodynamic equilibrium, but they can differ in plasmas sustained by an external source of energy.

4. The magnetic field. There may exist a magnetic field $\mathbf{B}_0$, into which the plasma is introduced and which is generated by an external source.

A more exact description of the plasma would make use of the electron and ion velocity distribution functions, and describe their time dependence by two Boltzmann equations. The macroscopic variables cited above are the first three moments of these distribution functions [1, p. 68], and their time dependence is governed by the hydrodynamic transport equations, that is, the conservation of particles and momentum. This hydrodynamic description is sufficient for the study of most phenomena. Some phenomena are more profitably studied with a microscopic theory. In those, a certain category of particles with a well determined velocity, and relatively small in number, have an effect which is more important than that of the remainder. For example, when the phase velocity v_ϕ of the observed waves is small, a nonnegligible fraction of the particles in the plasma may have a velocity in the neighborhood of v_ϕ. The over-all density and average velocity is then less important to describe the phenomenon than the density of that group of particles which accompany the wave [3].

Making use of the quantities introduced above, we define various descriptive frequencies.

$$\omega_p = (4\pi \bar{n}_e q_e^2 c^2 / m_e)^{1/2} \tag{5}$$

$$\Omega_p = (4\pi \bar{n}_i q_i^2 c^2 / m_i)^{1/2} \tag{6}$$

and a combination

$$\omega_0 = (\omega_p^2 + \Omega_p^2)^{1/2} \tag{7}$$

The gyromagnetic frequency of the electrons and the ions is

$$\omega_b = - q_e B_0 / m_e \tag{8}$$

$$\Omega_b = q_i B_0 / m_i \tag{9}$$

We note that these frequencies are related by

$$\omega_p{}^2 / \Omega_p{}^2 = \omega_b / \Omega_b = m_i / Z m_e \equiv m \tag{10}$$

1.2 Interaction Between Electromagnetic Field and Particles

The propagation of the wave in a plasma can be described in the general case by a perturbation of the descriptive variables which have just been defined and the electromagnetic fields $\mathbf{E}$, $\mathbf{B}$.[*] We shall represent the perturbed plasma state by means of the following variables: (1) electron density, $\overline{n}_e + n_e$; (2) ion density, $\overline{n}_i + n_i$; (3) average velocity of electrons, $\mathbf{v}_e$; (4) average velocity of ions, $\mathbf{v}_i$; (5) electron pressure, $\overline{p}_e + p_e$; and (6) ion pressure, $\overline{p}_i + p_i$.

The unbarred quantities n_e, n_i, $\mathbf{v}_e$, $\mathbf{v}_i$, p_e, p_i represent the perturbations as a function of space and time due to the passage of the waves; they should not be confused with the barred quantities $\overline{n}_e$, $\overline{n}_i$, $\overline{p}_e$, $\overline{p}_i$, which represent constant average values ($\overline{\mathbf{v}}_e = \overline{\mathbf{v}}_i = 0$). We shall limit ourselves to the study of waves of *small amplitude* in the sense that they result only in small amplitude variations in the parameters which describe the plasma.

The charge density can be defined as a function of these variables:

$$\sigma = n_e q_e + n_i q_i \tag{11}$$

The current vector is

$$\mathbf{J} = (\overline{n}_e + n_e) q_e \mathbf{v}_e + (\overline{n}_i + n_i) q_i \mathbf{v}_i \tag{12}$$

Since we consider only waves of small amplitude, expression (12) can be simplified by neglecting second order terms $n_e \mathbf{v}_e$, and $n_i \mathbf{v}_i$. We thus obtain

---

[*]The fluctuation in the electromagnetic due to thermal agitation will be neglected [4].

$$\mathbf{J} = \bar{n}_e q_e \mathbf{v}_e + \bar{n}_i q_i \mathbf{v}_i \tag{13}$$

To obtain waves that can propagate in a plasma, one must require that the electromagnetic field associated with the wave is caused by current and space charge which, in turn, result from the action of these fields on the plasma; it is a self-consistent field problem. The fields $\mathbf{E}$ and $\mathbf{B}$ are related to the current and to the space charge by Maxwell's equations which can be written in EMU.

$$\boldsymbol{\nabla} \times \mathbf{E} = - \partial \mathbf{B}/\partial t \tag{14}$$

$$\boldsymbol{\nabla} \cdot \mathbf{B} = 0 \tag{15}$$

$$\boldsymbol{\nabla} \times \mathbf{B} = 4\pi \mathbf{J} + (1/c^2)\,(\partial \mathbf{E}/\partial t) \tag{16}$$

$$\boldsymbol{\nabla} \cdot \mathbf{E} = 4\pi c^2 \sigma \tag{17}$$

The effect of the fields $\mathbf{E}$ and $\mathbf{B}$ on electrons and ions in the plasma is obtained from the conservation equation [1, pp. 91–93] which we linearize by neglecting second order terms. The equations of particle conservation are

$$\partial n_e/\partial t + \boldsymbol{\nabla} \cdot \bar{n}_e \mathbf{v}_e = 0 \tag{18}$$

$$\partial n_i/\partial t + \boldsymbol{\nabla} \cdot \bar{n}_i \mathbf{v}_i = 0 \tag{19}$$

the equations of momentum conservation are

$$\bar{n}_e m_e (\partial \mathbf{v}_e/\partial t) = \bar{n}_e q_e (\mathbf{E} + \mathbf{v}_e \times \mathbf{B}_0) - \nabla p_e + \mathbf{P}_{en} + \mathbf{P}_{ei} \tag{20}$$

$$\bar{n}_i m_i (\partial \mathbf{v}_i/\partial t) = \bar{n}_i q_i (\mathbf{E} + \mathbf{v}_i \times \mathbf{B}_0) - \nabla p_i + \mathbf{P}_{in} + \mathbf{P}_{ie} \tag{21}$$

In Eqs. (20) and (21) we have also neglected the action of the magnetic field of the wave on the particles, a common approximation. This approximation becomes invalid, as does all macroscopic theory, when the phase velocity of the waves is of the order of magnitude of the thermal speed.

The terms $\mathbf{P}_{en}$ and $\mathbf{P}_{in}$ represent the transfer of momentum due to collisions between charged and neutral particles; the terms $\mathbf{P}_{ei}$ and $\mathbf{P}_{ie}$ similarly represent the momentum exchange between electrons and ions due to collisions. We now assert that we can write the three terms in the form

$$\mathbf{P}_{en} = - \bar{n}_e m_e \nu_{en} \mathbf{v}_e \qquad (22)$$

$$\mathbf{P}_{in} = - \bar{n}_i m_i \nu_{in} \mathbf{v}_i \qquad (23)$$

$$\mathbf{P}_{ei} = - \mathbf{P}_{ie} = - \bar{n}_e m_e \nu (\mathbf{v}_e - \mathbf{v}_i) \qquad (24)$$

where ν_{en} and ν_{in} are the collision frequencies between charged and neutral particles and ν is the ion-electron collision frequency. The use of these scalar quantities is not always justifiable because the collision frequencies are, in general, tensor quantities [1, p. 100]. Furthermore, they cannot be clearly defined unless one knows the microscopic state of the fluid. We shall consider in this book Eqs. (22), (23), and (24) as phenomenological definitions of the collision frequencies.*

The expression used to determine the pressure tensor presents conceptional difficulties [1, p. 96]. In the interest of calculational simplicity, we assert that the perturbations caused by the wave are adiabatic and that we can write

$$\nabla p_e = \gamma_e K T_e \nabla \mathrm{n}_e = m_e V_e^2 \nabla \mathrm{n}_e \qquad (25)$$

$$\nabla \mathrm{p}_i = \gamma_i K T_i \nabla \mathrm{n}_i = m_i V_i^2 \nabla \mathrm{n}_i \qquad (26)$$

The average speeds of thermal motion of the electrons and ions are defined by means of Eqs. (27) and (28):

$$V_e^2 = \gamma_e K T_e / m_e \qquad (27)$$

$$V_i^2 = \gamma_i K T_i / m_i \qquad (28)$$

In Eqs. (25) through (28) K represents Boltzmann's constant.
Equations (25) and (26) are somewhat open to criticism. To be fully rigorous, they should be obtained from a more thorough examination of the macroscopic equation for the transfer of kinetic

---

*Equations (22) and (23) further assume that interaction of the neutral molecules is negligible, or that ordinary sound waves are not excited in the neutral gas by the motion of the plasma. We shall not discuss this hypothesis; we can, however, remark that this hypothesis is accurate in the limits where the mass of neutral molecules is well above that of the ions or when the frequency is very high. In any event this question does not arise in a completely ionized gas.

pressure [1, p. 94]. In any case, V_e and V_i are velocities in the neighborhood of the average thermal velocities. Also, the values of γ_e and γ_i are functions of the ratio of the wave frequency to the particle collision frequency. In most cases, however, this ratio is large and the particles undergo virtually no collisions during the compression generated by the wave. Since the compression is carried only in the direction of propagation, one may take $\gamma_e = \gamma_i = 3$ [2, p. 13].

CHAPTER 2

Dispersion Relation for Plane Waves

Under the conditions specified in the preceding chapter, a plasma is capable of propagating *four distinct modes of adiabatic oscillations** [5]. They shall be designated by the terms *ordinary, extraordinary, electron, and ion waves*. These modes are distinguished by the polarization and amplitude of the associated electromagnetic fields, and the motion of particles. This chapter concerns itself with the derivation of the dispersion relation for these four modes.

2.1 Properties of Monochromatic Plane Waves

To obtain a despersion relation we apply the equations of the preceding chapter to the specific case of a monochromatic plane wave which propagates in the positive z direction. The variables describing the wave are expressed in the form:

$$\mathbf{A} = A \exp \left[j(\omega t - kz) \right] \tag{1}$$

where A is, in general, a complex coefficient.

We use the following linear operators:

$$\partial/\partial t = j\omega \tag{2}$$

$$\boldsymbol{\nabla} = -jk \tag{3}$$

where k is the propagation vector in the z direction. Applying the operator $\boldsymbol{\nabla}$ to a vector $\mathbf{A}$,

---

*If one considers the effects of viscosity [6] or thermal conductivity [7], other modes of oscillation are obtained which we shall not treat in this book.

$$\nabla \cdot \mathbf{A} = -jk\mathrm{A}_z \tag{4}$$

$$\nabla \times \mathbf{A} = jk(\mathrm{A}_y\mathbf{i} - \mathrm{A}_x\mathbf{j}) \tag{5}$$

$$\nabla^2\mathbf{A} = -k^2\mathrm{A}_z\mathbf{k} \tag{6}$$

$$\nabla \times (\nabla \times \mathbf{A}) = k^2(\mathrm{A}_x\mathbf{i} + \mathrm{A}_y\mathbf{j}) = k^2\mathbf{A}_\perp \tag{7}$$

where $\mathbf{A}_\perp$ is the transverse component of the vector $\mathbf{A}$ (component perpendicular to the z axis).

When the wave number k is real, the wave propagates unattenuated with phase and group velocity

$$v_\phi = \omega/k \tag{8}$$

$$v_g = d\omega/dk \tag{9}$$

and k is related to the wave length λ by the equation

$$k = 2\pi/\lambda$$

If $k = \alpha - j\beta$ is complex, the wave propagates with phase velocity ω/α and continuously decreasing amplitude $A \exp(-\beta z)$ (positive β) in the quiescent plasmas under consideration. If $k = -j\beta$ is imaginary, the wave is evanescent and again its amplitude varies as $A \exp(-\beta z)$.

Maxwell's equations* (1.14) and (1.15) can be expressed using Eq. (5)

$$B_x = -kE_y/\omega \tag{10}$$

$$B_y = kE_x/\omega \tag{11}$$

$$B_z = 0 \tag{12}$$

which combine to give

$$B_xE_x + B_yE_y = 0 \tag{13}$$

These equations show that the magnetic field associated with the

---

*The system of cross reference used for equations and figures is as follows: Eq. (7.9) or Fig. 7.9 refers to equation or figure 9, respectively, in Chapter 7; Eq. (A2.7) refers to equation 7 in Appendix 2.

wave is transverse in all cases and orthogonal to the transverse component of the electric field. Let us now eliminate this oscillating magnetic field from Eqs. (1.14) and (1.16). This field interacts weakly with the particles and is therefore less important, in general, than the electric field of the wave. We obtain

$$\nabla \times \nabla \times \mathbf{E} + (1/c^2)(\partial^2 \mathbf{E}/\partial t^2) + 4\pi(\partial \mathbf{J}/\partial t) = 0 \qquad (14)$$

and introducing Eqs. (7) and (1.13)

$$\left(\frac{k^2 c^2}{\omega^2} - 1\right) E_x = \frac{4\pi c^2}{j\omega}\left(\bar{n}_e q_e v_{ex} + \bar{n}_i q_i v_{ix}\right) \qquad (15)$$

$$\left(\frac{k^2 c^2}{\omega^2} - 1\right) E_y = \frac{4\pi c^2}{j\omega}\left(\bar{n}_e q_e v_{ey} + \bar{n}_i q_i v_{iy}\right) \qquad (16)$$

$$- E_z = \frac{4\pi c^2}{j\omega}\left(\bar{n}_e q_e v_{ez} + \bar{n}_i q_i v_{iz}\right) \qquad (17)$$

When $k^2 c^2/\omega^2$ is real, these formulas show that vectors $\mathbf{J}$ and $\mathbf{E}$ are in quadrature. E_z is always retarded with respect to J_z; E_x and E_y are either advanced or retarded with respect to J_x and J_y depending upon whether $k^2 c^2/\omega^2$ is respectively smaller or greater than unity.

The equation for the conservation of electrons and ions can be written as

$$n_e = k\bar{n}_e v_{ez}/\omega \qquad (18)$$

$$n_i = k\bar{n}_i v_{iz}/\omega \qquad (19)$$

By substituting these expressions in Eqs. (1.25) and (1.26), the pressure gradients can be expressed as a function of the velocities $\mathbf{v}_e$ and $\mathbf{v}_i$. We thus eliminate the density fluctuation due to the wave and obtain

$$\nabla p_e = - jk\bar{n}_e m_e V_e^2 v_{ez}\mathbf{k}/\omega \qquad (20)$$

$$\nabla p_i = - jk\bar{n}_i m_i V_i^2 v_{iz}\mathbf{k}/\omega \qquad (21)$$

Without affecting the generality of the treatment, we shall now choose the axis so that the field $\mathbf{B}_0$ is located in the yz plane, and represent its two components B_z and B_y by B_L and B_T, respectively. The electron momentum conservation equation then is

$$j\omega\bar{n}_e m_e v_{ex} = \bar{n}_e q_e (E_x + v_{ey}B_L - v_{ez}B_T)$$
$$- \nu\bar{n}_e m_e (v_{ex} - v_{ix}) - \nu_{en}\bar{n}_e m_e v_{ex} \tag{22}$$

$$j\omega\bar{n}_e m_e v_{ey} = \bar{n}_e q_e (E_y - v_{ex}B_L)$$
$$- \nu\bar{n}_e m_e (v_{ey} - v_{iy}) - \nu_{en}\bar{n}_e m_e v_{ey} \tag{23}$$

$$j\omega\bar{n}_e m_e v_{ez} = \bar{n}_e q_e (E_z + v_{ex}B_T) - \nu\bar{n}_e m_e (v_{ez} - v_{iz})$$
$$- \nu_{en}\bar{n}_e m_e v_{ez} + j\frac{k^2}{\omega}\,\bar{n}_e m_e V_e^2 v_{ez} \tag{24}$$

The ion momentum conservation is expressed by three analogous equations. We shall not write these equations but shall label them (22'), (23'), and (24'). They are obtained from the three preceding equations by replacing all the subscripts e by the subscript i except in the electron-ion collision term which simply changes sign.

In principle, we can solve for the velocities from the six momentum transfer equations and obtain **J** as a function of **E** in the form

$$\mathbf{J} = |\sigma|\,\mathbf{E} \tag{25}$$

where $|\sigma|$ is the conductivity tensor for a plane wave. In addition, we often make use of the dielectric tensor:

$$|\epsilon| = 1 + (4\pi c^2/j\omega)|\sigma| \tag{26}$$

In general, when V_e and V_i are nonzero, $|\sigma|$ and $|\epsilon|$ depend on ω and k. The derivation is discussed in Appendix 1.

2.2   The General Dispersion Equation

The three wave equations (15), (16), and (17) together with the six equations for the conservation of momentum (22), (23), (24), (22'), (23'), and (24') form a homogeneous linear set with nine unknowns. These variables are the components of the vectors **E**, $\mathbf{v}_e$ and $\mathbf{v}_i$. For a solution to exist, the determinant of the set must be equal to zero. This determinant is represented in Table 2.1. In the first column we have the number of the equation on that row, and on the top line the variable to which each column corresponds, in the order which is the most logical and fruitful from the point of view of physical interpretation.

By setting this determinant equal to zero, we relate the propagation constant k to the frequency ω; this is called the dispersion equation; in general, it is a fourth order equation in k^2. The four roots correspond to four modes of propagation which are, in general, distinct. For each root of k^2 there are two conjugate solutions, giving two identical waves which propagate in opposite directions along the z axis.

A zero determinant remains null when all the terms of a given row or column are multiplied by the same factor. This property can be used to transform the determinant in Table 2.1. We effect such a transformation by multiplying the terms in the table by the factors shown on the right for each row, and by those at the bottom for each column. The resultant determinant is represented by Table 2.2. For simplicity we assume collisions to be negligible ($\nu = \nu_{en} = \nu_{in} = 0$). The multiplications performed on the columns are equivalent to dividing the variables by the respective factors. Therefore, we have indicated on the top line of Table 2.2 the new variables to which the terms in each column correspond. We have also introduced "longitudinal gyromagnetic frequencies" ω_L and Ω_L, and "transverse gyromagnetic frequencies" ω_T and Ω_T defined as ω_b and Ω_b but by substituting B_L and B_T for B.

The dispersion equation contained in Table 2.2 results from elimination of the current density and wave magnetic field $\boldsymbol{B}$ from the general equations. We could, using these equations, eliminate other variables and obtain dispersion equations in other forms. The choice of variables to be eliminated cannot be selected a priori, but should be adapted to the problem. In Appendix 2 and in Chapters 6–9, other equally useful forms of this equation will be found. Naturally, all these forms become identical when the corresponding determinants are expanded. The fully expanded form of the dispersion equation is studied in Chapter 6.

Table 2.1

Equations	Variables				
	E_x	v_{ex}	v_{ix}	E_y	v_{ey}
(15)	$j\left(\dfrac{k^2c^2}{\omega^2}-1\right)$	$-\dfrac{4\pi c^2\bar{n}_e q_e}{\omega}$	$-\dfrac{4\pi c^2\bar{n}_i q_i}{\omega}$	0	0
(22)	$\bar{n}_e q_e$	$-\bar{n}_e m_e(j\omega+\nu+\nu_{en})$	$\nu\bar{n}_e m_e$	0	$\bar{n}_e q_e B_L$
(22′)	$\bar{n}_i q_i$	$\nu\bar{n}_e m_e$	$-\bar{n}_i m_i(j\omega+\nu_{in})-\nu\bar{n}_e m_e$	0	0
(16)	0	0	0	$j\left(\dfrac{k^2c^2}{\omega^2}-1\right)$	$-\dfrac{4\pi c^2\bar{n}_e q_e}{\omega}$
(23)	0	$-\bar{n}_e q_e B_L$	0	$\bar{n}_e q_e$	$-\bar{n}_e m_e(j\omega+\nu+\nu_{en})$
(23′)	0	0	$-\bar{n}_i q_i B_L$	$\bar{n}_i q_i$	$\nu\bar{n}_e m_e$
(17)	0	0	0	0	0
(24)	0	$\bar{n}_e q_e B_T$	0	0	0
(24′)	0	0	$\bar{n}_i q_i B_T$	0	0
	1	$j\dfrac{q_e}{m_e\omega}$	$j\dfrac{q_i}{m_i\omega}$	$-j$	$\dfrac{q_e}{m_e\omega}$

Table 2.1 (continued)

Variables				
v_{iy}	E_z	v_{ez}	v_{iz}	
0	0	0	0	j
0	0	$-\bar{n}_e q_e B_T$	0	$\dfrac{1}{\bar{n}_e q_e}$
$\bar{n}_i q_i B_L$	0	0	$-\bar{n}_i q_i B_T$	$\dfrac{1}{\bar{n}_i q_i}$
$-\dfrac{4\pi c^2 \bar{n}_e q_i}{\omega}$	0	0	0	-1
$\nu \bar{n}_e m_e$	0	0	0	$\dfrac{j}{\bar{n}_e q_e}$
$-\bar{n}_i m_i(j\omega + \nu_{in}) - \nu\bar{n}_e m_e$	0	0	0	$\dfrac{j}{\bar{n}_i q_i}$
0	$-j$	$-\dfrac{4\pi c^2 \bar{n}_e q_e}{\omega}$	$-\dfrac{4\pi c^2 \bar{n}_i q_i}{\omega}$	-1
0	$\bar{n}_e q_e$	$-\bar{n}_e m_e(j\omega + \nu + \nu_{en}) + \bar{n}_e m_e j \dfrac{k^2}{\omega} V_e^2$	$\nu \bar{n}_e m_e$	$\dfrac{j}{\bar{n}_e q_e}$
0	$\bar{n}_i q_i$	$\nu \bar{n}_e m_e$	$-\bar{n}_i m_i\left(j\omega + \nu_{in} - j\dfrac{k^2}{\omega} V_i^2\right) - \bar{n}_e m_e \nu$	$\dfrac{j}{\bar{n}_i q_i}$
$\dfrac{q_i}{m_i \omega}$	$-j$	$\dfrac{q_e}{m_e \omega}$	$\dfrac{q_i}{m_i \omega}$	Multipliers

Table 2.2

| | | Variables | | | | | | | |
Equations	E_x	$\dfrac{v_{ex}}{j}\dfrac{m_e\omega}{q_e}$	$\dfrac{v_{ix}}{j}\dfrac{m_i\omega}{q_i}$	jE_y	$v_{ey}\dfrac{m_e\omega}{q_e}$	$v_{iy}\dfrac{m_i\omega}{q_i}$	jE_z	$v_{ez}\dfrac{m_e\omega}{q_e}$	$v_{iz}\dfrac{m_i\omega}{q_i}$
(15)	$1-\dfrac{k^2c^2}{\omega^2}$	$\dfrac{\omega_p^2}{\omega^2}$	$\dfrac{\Omega_p^2}{\omega^2}$	0	0	0	0	0	0
(22)	1	1	0	0	$-\dfrac{\omega_L}{\omega}$	0	0	$\dfrac{\omega_T}{\omega}$	0
(22')	1	0	1	0	0	$\dfrac{\Omega_L}{\omega}$	0	0	$-\dfrac{\Omega_T}{\omega}$
(16)	0	0	0	$1-\dfrac{k^2c^2}{\omega^2}$	$\dfrac{\omega_p^2}{\omega^2}$	$\dfrac{\Omega_p^2}{\omega^2}$	0	0	0
(23)	0	$-\dfrac{\omega_L}{\omega}$	0	1	1	0	0	0	0
(23')	0	0	$\dfrac{\Omega_L}{\omega}$	1	0	1	0	0	0
(17)	0	0	0	0	0	0	1	$\dfrac{\omega_p^2}{\omega^2}$	$\dfrac{\Omega_p^2}{\omega^2}$
(24)	0	$\dfrac{\omega_T}{\omega}$	0	0	0	0	1	$1-\dfrac{k^2V_e^2}{\omega^2}$	0
(24')	0	0	$-\dfrac{\Omega_T}{\omega}$	0	0	0	1	0	$1-\dfrac{k^2V_i^2}{\omega^2}$

2.3   Singularities in the Dispersion Equation

The dispersion equation expressed by the determinant in Table 2.2 enables us to study certain specific cases which exhibit waves of a rather simple structure.

a. Case where B_0 is zero. Linearly polarized transverse waves; longitudinal waves. To begin, when the magnetic field is zero, the dispersion relation becomes.

$$
\begin{vmatrix}
 & & & 0 & 0 & 0 & 0 & 0 & 0 \\
 & \Delta_1 & & 0 & 0 & 0 & 0 & 0 & 0 \\
 & & & 0 & 0 & 0 & 0 & 0 & 0 \\
0 & 0 & 0 & & & & 0 & 0 & 0 \\
0 & 0 & 0 & & \Delta_1 & & 0 & 0 & 0 \\
0 & 0 & 0 & & & & 0 & 0 & 0 \\
0 & 0 & 0 & 0 & 0 & 0 & & & \\
0 & 0 & 0 & 0 & 0 & 0 & & \Delta_L & \\
0 & 0 & 0 & 0 & 0 & 0 & & &
\end{vmatrix}
= \Delta_1{}^2 \Delta_L = 0 \qquad (27)
$$

This equation is a product of three factors, of which the first two are identical. If ω and k are such that the first factor Δ_1 is zero, a solution for the system emerges in which E_x, v_{ex}, and v_{ix} differ from zero while the other six variables vanish. In other words, the wave in question has a linear transverse polarization parallel to the x axis. From the form of Eq. (27) there exists an identical wave polarized in the y direction.

If ω and k are chosen so that the third factor, Δ_L, vanishes, we obtain a solution in which the only nonzero variables are E_z, v_{ez}, and v_{iz}. This means a wave polarized parallel to the z axis, that is, purely longitudinal. The determinant Δ_L is quadratic in k^2 so that there exist two longitudinal waves. In Chapter 4 it will be shown that, at the extremes of frequency these two waves become respectively electron plasma oscillations and a pseudosonic wave.

b. Case where B_0 is longitudinal; existence of two distinct transverse waves. When there exists a longitudinal magnetic field, the dispersion equation is expressed in the form:

$$
\begin{vmatrix}
\Delta_1 & \begin{matrix} 0 & 0 & 0 \\ 0 & -\dfrac{\omega_L}{\omega} & 0 \\ 0 & 0 & \dfrac{\Omega_L}{\omega} \end{matrix} & \begin{matrix} 0 & 0 & 0 \\ 0 & 0 & 0 \\ 0 & 0 & 0 \end{matrix} \\[2em]
\begin{matrix} 0 & 0 & 0 \\ 0 & -\dfrac{\omega_L}{\omega} & 0 \\ 0 & 0 & \dfrac{\Omega_L}{\omega} \end{matrix} & \Delta_1 & \begin{matrix} 0 & 0 & 0 \\ 0 & 0 & 0 \\ 0 & 0 & 0 \end{matrix} \\[2em]
\begin{matrix} 0 & 0 & 0 \\ 0 & 0 & 0 \\ 0 & 0 & 0 \end{matrix} & \begin{matrix} 0 & 0 & 0 \\ 0 & 0 & 0 \\ 0 & 0 & 0 \end{matrix} & \Delta_L
\end{vmatrix} = \Delta_T \Delta_L = 0 \quad (28)
$$

where Δ_T designates the 6×6 determinant delineated by the double lines.

It is immediately obvious from this form that the longitudinal waves are not altered by the presence of a longitudinal magnetic field. This magnetic field, however, introduces a coupling between the two transverse waves previously discovered. The result is two distinct waves which have both E_x, v_{ex}, v_{ix} and E_y, v_{ey}, v_{iy} components. We shall see in Chapter 3 that these waves are circularly polarized in the xy plane.

c. B_0 arbitrary. Coupling between transverse and longitudinal waves. Finally, by referring once more to Table 2.2 we see that a transverse magnetic field couples the two transverse with the two longitudinal waves. There appear, therefore, four modes of propagation which have, in general, nonzero components in all three directions. There exist no longer purely longitudinal or transverse waves. The general discussion of the dispersion relation is then fairly complex (Chapter 6). We can, however, study a certain number of relatively simple cases:

1. Purely transverse propagation: $\omega_L = \Omega_L = 0$ (Chapter 7).
2. Cold plasmas: $V_e = V_i = 0$ (Chapter 8).
3. High frequency waves in cold plasma: Appleton-Hartree equation (Chapter 8).
4. Low frequency or magnetodynamic waves* (Chapter 9).

Previous studies of the propagation of waves in plasmas have essentially dealt with these singular cases. They have resulted in a mild anarchy of nomenclature for the various types of waves, which is nevertheless convenient and has been sanctified through use. The general study which we develop in Chapter 6 leads to a more natural nomenclature for the four modes, which does not always coincide with the generally adopted definitions. In the conflicting situations, we shall warn the reader against possible confusion.

2.4 General Notation

Throughout this volume we shall use the following notation:

$$\omega_p^2 = 4\pi \bar{n}_e q_e^2 c^2 / m_e \tag{29}$$

$$\Omega_p^2 = 4\pi \bar{n}_i q_i^2 c^2 / m_i \tag{30}$$

$$\omega_0^2 = \omega_p^2 + \Omega_p^2 \tag{31}$$

$$\omega_b = - q_e B_0 / m_e \tag{32}$$

$$\Omega_b = q_i B_0 / m_i \tag{33}$$

$$m = \omega_p^2 / \Omega_p^2 = \omega_b / \Omega_b = m_i / Z m_e \tag{34}$$

$$A = \frac{\omega_p^2 + \Omega_p^2}{\omega_b \Omega_b} = \frac{\omega_p^2}{\omega_b^2} + \frac{\Omega_p^2}{\Omega_b^2} = \frac{4\pi c^2 (\bar{n}_e m_e + \bar{n}_i m_i)}{B_0^2} \tag{35}$$

$$V_e^2 = \gamma_e K T_e / m_e \tag{36}$$

---

*In the literature these waves are also called magnetohydrodynamic or hydromagnetic. We think that the prefix "hydro," which by contrast to "aero" relates to liquids, ought not be retained.

$$V_i^2 = \gamma_i K T_i / m_i \tag{37}$$

$$\tau = \gamma_i T_i / Z \gamma_e T_e = m V_i^2 / V_e^2 = m \epsilon_e / \epsilon_i \tag{38}$$

$$V_s^2 = \frac{\Omega_p^2 V_e^2 + \omega_p^2 V_i^2}{\omega_p^2 + \Omega_p^2} = \frac{\bar{n}_e m_e V_e^2 + \bar{n}_i m_i V_i^2}{\bar{n}_e m_e + \bar{n}_i m_i} \tag{39}$$

$$\epsilon_e = c^2 / V_e^2 \tag{40}$$

$$\epsilon_i = c^2 / V_i^2 \tag{41}$$

$$\epsilon_s = c^2 / V_s^2 \tag{42}$$

$$\epsilon_a = 1 + A = c^2 / V_a^2 \tag{43}$$

$$x = \omega_0^2 / \omega^2 \tag{44}$$

$$y = k^2 c^2 / \omega^2 \tag{45}$$

CHAPTER 3

Transverse Electromagnetic Waves ($B_T = 0$)

We have seen in Chapter 2 that when the transverse magnetic field B_T is zero, there exist two transverse and two longitudinal waves. In this chapter, we treat the properties of the transverse waves. Our principal concern will be the structure of the perturbations in the plasma. In our study of these waves, we shall consider primarily the propagation speed; the attenuation will not be observed as we shall set

$$\nu = \nu_{en} = \nu_{in} = 0 \tag{1}$$

3.1 General Equations — Ordinary and Extraordinary Waves

a. Dispersion relation. The dispersion relation can be computed from the determinant Δ_T formed by the first six rows and columns of Table (2.2). It may be seen directly that thermal motion plays no role in the properties of transverse waves.

In Chapter 6 we shall perform the expansion of the determinant. Here we eliminate the components of v_e and v_i from Eqs. (15), (16), (22), (23), (22'), and (23') of Chapter 2. For example, invoking the conditions $E_z = v_{ez} = v_{iz} = 0$, we obtain from the last four of these equations

$$v_{ex}(\omega_L{}^2 - \omega^2) = q_e(j\omega E_x - \omega_L E_y)/m_e \tag{2}$$

$$v_{ey}(\omega_L{}^2 - \omega^2) = q_e(j\omega E_y + \omega_L E_x)/m_e \tag{3}$$

$$v_{ix}(\Omega_L{}^2 - \omega^2) = q_i(j\omega E_x + \Omega_L E_y)/m_i \tag{4}$$

$$v_{iy}(\Omega_L{}^2 - \omega^2) = q_i(j\omega E_y - \Omega_L E_x)/m_i \tag{5}$$

19

In the above equations the same sign convention has been used as in relations (1.8) and (1.9). In other words, ω_L and Ω_L are positive when B_L is positive, as will be assumed throughout to simplify the treatment; the modifications which apply to the results when B_L is negative will be obvious. By eliminating the components of velocity from Eqs. (2), (3), (4), (5), (2.15) and (2.16), we easily obtain the following two expressions for the ratio E_y/E_x

$$\frac{E_y}{E_x} = -\frac{\dfrac{\omega_p{}^2\omega_L}{\omega^2 - \omega_L{}^2} - \dfrac{\Omega_p{}^2\Omega_L}{\omega^2 - \Omega_L{}^2}}{j\omega\left[\dfrac{k^2c^2}{\omega^2} - 1 + \dfrac{\omega_p{}^2}{\omega^2 - \omega_L{}^2} + \dfrac{\Omega_p{}^2}{\omega^2 - \Omega_L{}^2}\right]}$$

$$= \frac{j\omega\left[\dfrac{k^2c^2}{\omega^2} - 1 + \dfrac{\omega_p{}^2}{\omega^2 - \omega_L{}^2} + \dfrac{\Omega_p{}^2}{\omega^2 - \Omega_L{}^2}\right]}{\dfrac{\omega_p{}^2\omega_L}{\omega^2 - \omega_L{}^2} - \dfrac{\Omega_p{}^2\Omega_L}{\omega^2 - \Omega_L{}^2}} \tag{6}$$

From these we obtain the compatibility condition

$$\omega\left(\frac{k^2c^2}{\omega^2} - 1 + \frac{\omega_p{}^2}{\omega^2 - \omega_L{}^2} + \frac{\Omega_p{}^2}{\omega^2 - \Omega_L{}^2}\right)$$
$$= \pm\left(\frac{\omega_p{}^2\omega_L}{\omega^2 - \omega_L{}^2} - \frac{\Omega_p{}^2\Omega_L}{\omega^2 - \Omega_L{}^2}\right) \tag{7}$$

Equation (7) is the dispersion relation for transverse waves. Throughout the rest of this book, we shall present the dispersion curves in terms of the dimensionless variables

$$x = (\omega_p{}^2 + \Omega_p{}^2)/\omega^2 = \omega_0{}^2/\omega^2 \tag{8}$$

$$y = k^2c^2/\omega^2 \tag{9}$$

The variable y is the square of the index of refraction. Let y_I and y_{II} represent the two solutions of Eq. (7). These are easily shown to be

$$y_I = 1 - [\omega_0{}^2/(\omega + \omega_L)(\omega - \Omega_L)] \tag{10}$$

$$y_{II} = 1 - [\omega_0{}^2/(\omega - \omega_L)(\omega + \Omega_L)] \tag{11}$$

It is common usage to refer to the wave y_I as the ordinary and to y_{II} as the extraordinary wave. We shall see in Chapter 5 that the study of waves that propagate in an arbitrary direction with respect to the magnetic field leads to the introduction of another definition for the ordinary and extraordinary modes, which we shall designate by y_1 and y_2 in order to avoid confusion. The two definitions become identical in the high frequency region. In the other frequency regions, in order to maintain clarity, we shall always use the words ordinary and extraordinary accompanied by the more precise designation y_I and y_{II} or y_1 and y_2.

b. Polarization of the two waves. It is worthwhile to differentiate the waves y_I and y_{II} by a simple physical characteristic. We can calculate E_y/E_x by substituting for y in Eq. (6) its value obtained from Eq. (7)

$$E_y/E_x = + j \qquad \text{for the ordinary wave } y_I$$
$$E_y/E_x = - j \qquad \text{for the extraordinary wave } y_{II} \tag{12}$$

Thus the two waves are circularly polarized in opposite sense. The electric vector of the extraordinary wave y_{II} rotates in the same sense as the electron gyromagnetic motion (Fig. 3.1). We can therefore see that this wave will be strongly perturbed by the elec-

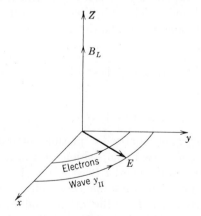

Fig. 3.1.

tron current when its frequency is of the order of the electron gyro-magnetic frequency. This strong interaction is represented by the term $1/(\omega - \omega_L)$ in y_{II}; ω_L is a resonant frequency for the extra-ordinary wave y_{II}. The ordinary wave, y_{I}, whose electric vector rotates in the same sense as the ions, has a resonance at the frequency $\omega = \Omega_L$.

Equations (2.15) and (2.16) show that the current $\mathbf{J}$ is also circularly polarized and advanced or retarded with respect to the vector $\mathbf{E}$ depending on whether y is smaller or greater than unity.

c. Dispersion curves. The dispersion curves in the plane of the coordinates x and y for the waves y_{I} and y_{II} have the shape shown in Fig. 3.2. The general curve is of fourth degree, and it shows two vertical asymptotes corresponding to the frequencies $\omega = \omega_L$ and $\omega = \Omega_L$. The index of refraction of the wave y_{I} goes to zero at the point R for the critical frequency

$$\omega_1 = \tfrac{1}{2}\{[(\omega_L + \Omega_L)^2 + 4\omega_0^2]^{1/2} - (\omega_L - \Omega_L)\} \qquad (13)$$

For the wave y_{II}, the index goes to zero at Q for the critical frequency

$$\omega_2 = \tfrac{1}{2}\{[(\omega_L + \Omega_L)^2 + 4\omega_0^2]^{1/2} + (\omega_L - \Omega_L)\} \qquad (14)$$

To discuss the dispersion curves, it is convenient to make use of the parameters A and m defined in Chapter 2 so that we can write the dispersion relations in the following form

$$\frac{y_{\mathrm{I}} - 1}{A} = \frac{x/A}{(\sqrt{x/A} + 1/\sqrt{m})(\sqrt{x/A} - \sqrt{m})} \qquad (15)$$

$$\frac{y_{\mathrm{II}} - 1}{A} = \frac{x/A}{(\sqrt{x/A} - 1/\sqrt{m})(\sqrt{x/A} + \sqrt{m})} \qquad (16)$$

We see that dispersion curves for plasmas of different density (A variable) but of a fixed composition (m constant) are homo-thetic with respect to the point I ($x = 0$, $y = 1$). This important property can be put to use in a diagram such as Fig. 3.2. In this diagram we have taken I as the origin and x/A, $(y - 1)/A$ as coordinates. This results in a universal dispersion curve (inde-

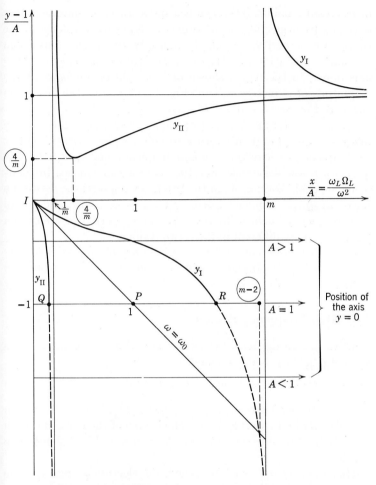

Fig. 3.2. Normalized dispersion curve: transverse waves.

pendent of A). Actually the curve in Fig. 3.2 is only a schematic drawing. Because, in general, the range of values of m is large, it is impossible to represent the whole dispersion curve on the same scale. Therefore, we have indicated on the diagram the coordinates of interesting points. The encircled quantities are limiting values obtained by neglecting higher orders in $1/m$. To transform to the coordinates x and y, we simply multiply the values marked in Fig. 3.2 by the factor A and move the horizontal axis. The new $y = 0$ axis moves to the region shown on the right of the figure as the magnitude of A increases. Thus Fig. 3.2 represents the dispersion curve for the case $A = 1$.

We see that for any A, the dispersion curves never intersect the line $y = 1$ except at point I. All waves have a phase velocity $v_\phi > c$ for frequencies above the resonant frequency and $v_\phi < c$ for frequencies below resonance. For the sake of convenience in treatment, we shall distinguish, in the two following sections, between a region of "high frequency" defined by $\omega \sim \omega_L \gg \Omega_L$, and one of "low frequency" defined by $\omega \ll \Omega_L$. The properties of waves in a plasma are very different in these two regions.

Exact dispersion curves for $m = 1836$ are plotted in Figs. 6.6–6.10, where the coordinates used are defined by Eqs. (6.30) and (6.31).

3.2 High Frequency Region

a. No magnetic field. Let us first note that in the absence of a magnetic field $\omega_L = \Omega_L = 0$ and

$$y_I = y_{II} = 1 - (\omega_0^2/\omega^2) \qquad (17)$$

The dispersion curve degenerates to the line IP (Fig. 3.2), which describes both of two solutions. (The degree of the curve has been reduced by two since the two top branches of Fig. 3.2 move to infinity.)

Therefore, regardless of frequency, the electron current has the dominant influence on the propagation of the two modes. It can also be shown that, in this case, E_y/E_x is indeterminate; a wave having any linear or elliptic polarization may be propagated through the plasma. In fact, we have already alluded to this simple case in Chapter 2 where we observed that there exists two identical modes linearly polarized one along the x axis, the other along the y

axis. Since these two modes have the same speed, they can be superimposed to give any polarization whatever. Only the waves of frequency $\omega > \omega_0$ correspond to a real index of refraction ($y > 0$) and propagate without attenuation. Those of frequency $\omega < \omega_0$ ($y < 0$) are evanescent. The frequency

$$\omega_0 = (\omega_p{}^2 + \Omega_p{}^2)^{1/2} \simeq \omega_p \qquad (18)$$

is called the critical frequency of the plasma or plasma frequency.*

b. Magnetic field present. When $\omega \gg \Omega_L \neq 0$, one obtains

$$y_I, y_{II} = 1 - [\omega_p{}^2/\omega(\omega \pm \omega_L)] \qquad (19)$$

In the frequency region in which $y > 0$, the phase velocity of the two circularly polarized waves differ. The medium is birefractive. A linearly polarized wave cannot propagate without transformation and demonstrates the Faraday effect. The wave can be decomposed into right and left handed circularly polarized waves. Since these two waves propagate with different speeds, they undergo a relative change of phase. When recombined to form a linearly polarized wave, one obtains, by applying Fresnel construction, a direction of polarization different from the initial direction. To conclude, the plane of polarization of a linearly polarized wave rotates as it propagates. One can see in Fig. 3.2 or in Eq. (19) that this birefractive effect goes to zero as one approaches point I; this occurs when the frequency approaches infinity or the magnetic field becomes small. In this case, a linearly polarized wave can propagate in any direction without transformation of the plane of polarization.

3.3 Low Frequency Region—Alfvén Waves

a. Limits of the index of refraction. Let us now consider the case where the frequency is well below the ion gyromagnetic fre-

---

*Some authors refer to ω_p as the "plasma frequency." However, as is clear from the present development, ω_p is the "plasma frequency" only to zeroth order in the ratio of the electron-to-ion mass.

quency. Figure (3.2) shows that the two curves for the index of refraction converge asymptotically. One thus obtains a second case of degeneracy where circularly polarized waves go into linearly polarized oscillations. Also, by setting $\omega = 0$ in Eq. (10) or Eq. (11), one quickly obtains the limit of the square of the index

$$y = 1 + (\omega_0^2/\omega_L\Omega_L) \tag{20}$$

Let V_a represent the limit of the phase velocity.
Then

$$y = c^2/V_a^2 = 1 + A = \epsilon_a \tag{21}$$

where V_a is called the Alfvén velocity. Equations (20) and (21) can also be rewritten as

$$\epsilon_a = 1 + (4\pi\rho c^2/B_L^2) \tag{22}$$

where

$$\rho = \bar{n}_e m_e + \bar{n}_i m_i \tag{23}$$

b. Discussion. Dense plasma; magnetodynamic approximation. When the plasma density is small or the magnetic field strong, $A \ll 1$ and the Alfvén speed is essentially c although always somewhat smaller. On the other hand, for dense plasmas or weak field $A \gg 1$ which yields

$$c^2/V_a^2 \simeq A \simeq \Omega_p^2/\Omega_L^2 \gg 1 \tag{24}$$

The Alfvén speed is then considerably smaller than that of light.

$$V_a \simeq c\Omega_L/\Omega_p \simeq B_L/(4\pi\rho)^{1/2} \tag{25}$$

Most of the plasmas we encounter have $A > 1$. We have listed in Table 3.1 values of V_a and A for some typical plasmas.

Referring to the basic equations in Chapter 2, one can see that for $A \gg 1$ the displacement current in the wave is negligible in comparison with the charge current. This regime represents the magnetodynamic approximation.

c. Linearly polarized waves. In the low frequency regime, for all plasma densities, the fact that both circular modes propagate with

Table 3.1

	Ionosphere	Discharges in air	Thermonuclear discharges	Solar corona	Interstellar clouds
B_0	0.5	$10^2 - 10^4$	$10^3 - 10^5$	$1 - 10^2$	10^{-5}
$\bar{n}_e$	10^4	10^{10}	10^{15}	10^8	10^3
$\dfrac{\bar{n}_e}{B_0^2}$	4×10^4	$10^6 - 10^2$	$10^9 - 10^5$	$10^8 - 10^4$	10^{13}
Type of ions m_i	O_2^+, N_2^+ 50×10^{-24}	O_2^+, N_2^+ 50×10^{-24}	d 3.3×10^{-24}	p 1.7×10^{-24}	p 1.7×10^{-24}
V_a	2×10^8	$4 \times 10^7 - 4 \times 10^9$	$5 \times 10^6 - 5 \times 10^8$	$2.2 \times 10^7 - 2.2 \times 10^9$	7×10^4
A	2.2×10^4	$5.6 \times 10^5 - 5.6 \times 10^{11}$	$3.6 \times 10^7 - 3.6 \times 10^3$	$1.4 \times 10^6 - 1.4 \times 10^2$	4.3×10^{11}

equal velocity implies that there is no Faraday effect. A linearly polarized plane wave propagates without rotation of the plane of polarization. It is instructive to extract this result in a straightforward manner. Consider a plane wave linearly polarized along the x axis. As we have $\omega \ll \Omega_L \ll \omega_L$, Eqs. (2), (3), (4), and (5) become

$$\bar{n}_e q_e v_{ex} = (\omega_p{}^2/4\pi c^2 \omega_L{}^2)j\omega E_x \tag{26}$$

$$\bar{n}_e q_e v_{ey} = (\omega_p{}^2/4\pi c^2 \omega_L{}^2)\omega_L E_x \tag{27}$$

$$\bar{n}_i q_i v_{ix} = (\Omega_p{}^2/4\pi c^2 \Omega_L{}^2)j\omega E_x \tag{28}$$

$$\bar{n}_i q_i v_{iy} = -(\Omega_p{}^2/4\pi c^2 \Omega_L{}^2)\Omega_L E_x \tag{29}$$

from which we obtain

$$J_x = \frac{j\omega E_x}{4\pi c^2}\left(\frac{\omega_p{}^2}{\omega_L{}^2} + \frac{Q_p{}^2}{\Omega_L{}^2}\right) = j\omega \frac{\rho}{B_L{}^2} E_x \tag{30}$$

$$4\pi J_x = \frac{A}{c^2}\frac{\partial E_x}{\partial t} \tag{31}$$

$$J_y = \frac{E_x}{4\pi c^2}\left(\frac{\omega_p{}^2}{\omega_L} - \frac{\Omega_p{}^2}{\Omega_L}\right) = 0 \tag{32}$$

We see that the current reduces simply to its J_x component which is 90° out of phase with E_x. From Eq. (31) the plane wave propagates as in an isotropic medium of dielectric constant $\epsilon_a = 1 + A$.

These results stem from the fact that the frequency ω is small compared to the gyromagnetic frequencies of ions and electrons. Consequently, we can consider the field E_x as remaining constant while the charges undergo many gyrations in the magnetic field. The charged particles, under the influence of E_x and B_L move with the same drift velocity in the y direction given by (see Fig. 3.3 and [1], p. 52)

$$\mathbf{v} = \mathbf{E} \times \mathbf{B}_L/B_L{}^2 \tag{33}$$

In our chosen axes, this velocity oscillates out of phase with the electric field and with amplitude

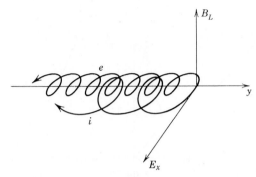

Fig. 3.3.

$$|v_y| = E_x/B_L \qquad (34)$$

This gives no net current but a total displacement of the fluid. This is equivalent to stating that the y component of the current represents the Hall effect. It is well known [1, p. 55] that the electron and ion components of the Hall effect tend to compensate each other exactly in a strong magnetic field. On the other hand, the x components are additive but are greatly reduced by a strong magnetic field along the z axis; this is the phenomenon of magnetoresistance. The result is a weak current inversely proportional to the square of the magnetic field. It is easy to see, by comparing Eq. (26) with Eq. (28), that the current is due primarily to ions.

We are now equipped to verify a fundamental property of plasmas. Let us assume that the plasma has an infinite conductivity and is placed in a strong magnetic field. We shall now show that, for a sufficiently slow rate of displacement of the plasma, the magnetic lines of force are carried along by the fluid. In other words, the lines of force are frozen in the plasma.

The oscillation E_x which produces a motion v_y is associated with a magnetic field

$$B_y = kE_x/\omega \qquad (35)$$

which is opposite to v_y. When the field B_y is added to the applied field B_L (see Fig. 3.4a, 3.4b), the lines of force take the sinusoidal

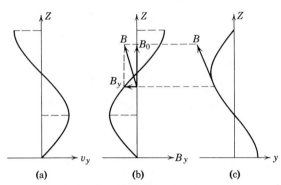

Fig. 3.4. Distortion of lines of force by an Alfvén wave.

shape seen in Fig. (3.4c). At any instant, the equation for the lines of force is

$$\frac{dy}{dz} = \frac{B_y}{B_L} \tag{36}$$

from which

$$y = (j/k)\,(B_y/B_L) + \text{Constant} \tag{37}$$

The motion of the fluid is described by

$$dy/dt = v_y = -\,E_x/B_L = -\,(\omega/k)\,(B_y/B_L) \tag{38}$$

from which the displacement is

$$y = (j/k)\,(B_y/B_L) + \text{Constant} \tag{39}$$

We thus confirm directly that a perturbed line of force can be represented by an unperturbed line shifted by jB_y/kB_L; this is equal to the displacement of the fluid. The behavior is as if the lines of force were elastic threads tied to the fluid and carried by it.

We can even push this analogy further. We will show that Alfvén waves can be considered as vibrations of magnetic tubes of force loaded by the mass of the fluid. We can consider the plasma contained in such a tube of force of uniform strength B_L as undergoing a tension $B_L{}^2/4\pi$ [9, p. 10] along the z axis and an isotropic pressure $B_L^2/8\pi$. This pressure plays no role in the case of transverse waves and the relation for vibrating strings applied to the magnetized plasma threads becomes

$$\rho(\partial^2 y/\partial t^2) = (B_L^2/4\pi) \, (\partial^2 y/\partial z^2) \qquad (40)$$

from which we obtain again the speed of propagation

$$v_\phi = B_L/(4\pi\rho)^{1/2} \qquad (41)$$

CHAPTER 4

Longitudinal Waves ($B_T = 0$)

In this chapter we devote our attention to two purely longitudinal waves which can propagate in the plasma when $B_T = 0$, that is, when the direction of propagation is along the magnetic field. The dispersion relations can be obtained by setting the determinant formed by the last three rows and columns of Table 2.2 to zero. We observe immediately that the thermal motion of the particles has an effect on the properties of longitudinal waves, whereas it does not enter in the case of transverse waves. As in the preceding chapter we shall neglect collisions and set

$$\nu = \nu_{en} = \nu_{in} = 0 \tag{1}$$

4.1 General Relations

a. Dispersion equation and curve. Consequently, we write the dispersion relation

$$\Delta_L = \begin{vmatrix} 1 & \dfrac{\omega_p{}^2}{\omega^2} & \dfrac{\Omega_p{}^2}{\omega^2} \\[2ex] 1 & 1 - \dfrac{k^2 V_e{}^2}{\omega^2} & 0 \\[2ex] 1 & 0 & 1 - \dfrac{k^2 V_i{}^2}{\omega^2} \end{vmatrix} = 0 \tag{2}$$

Rather than solving the determinant directly, we first calculate the physically interesting quantity v_{iz}/v_{ez}. From Table 2.2 the variables which correspond to the two last columns are $v_{ez}m_e\omega/q_e$ and $v_{iz}m_i\omega/q_i$ We recall that the ratio of these two variables is $-mv_{iz}/v_{ez}$ because of the signs associated with the charges.

For a set of homogeneous linear equations the ratio of two variables is the ratio of the minors associated with the corresponding elements on any row, carrying the appropriate sign. By applying this rule successively to the three rows of determinant (2), we obtain

$$- m\frac{v_{iz}}{v_{ez}} = -\frac{k^2 V_e^2 - \omega^2}{k^2 V_i^2 - \omega^2} \tag{3}$$

$$= \frac{\omega_p^2}{k^2 V_i^2 - \omega^2 + \Omega_p^2} \tag{3'}$$

$$= \frac{k^2 V_e^2 - \omega^2 + \omega_p^2}{\Omega_p^2} \tag{3''}$$

By combining the two previous expressions, we now obtain the dispersion relation:

$$(k^2 V_e^2 - \omega^2 + \omega_p^2)(k^2 V_i^2 - \omega^2 + \Omega_p^2) - \omega_p^2 \Omega_p^2 = 0 \tag{4}$$

or

$$\left(y\,\frac{V_e^2}{c^2} - 1\right)\left(y\,\frac{V_i^2}{c^2} - 1\right) + \frac{\omega_p^2}{\omega^2}\left(y\,\frac{V_i^2}{c^2} - 1\right)$$
$$+ \frac{\Omega_p^2}{\omega^2}\left(y\,\frac{V_e^2}{c^2} - 1\right) = 0 \tag{5}$$

By substituting

$$V_s^2 = (\omega_p^2 V_i^2 + \Omega_p^2 V_e^2)/(\omega_p^2 + \Omega_p^2) \tag{6}$$

it becomes

$$\left(y\,\frac{V_e^2}{c^2} - 1\right)\left(y\,\frac{V_i^2}{c^2} - 1\right) + \frac{\omega_0^2}{\omega^2}\left(y\,\frac{V_s^2}{c^2} - 1\right) = 0 \tag{7}$$

Using the notation given by Eqs. (2.40) to (2.42), we can finally express the dispersion relation in the form

$$x = -\frac{\left(y\,\dfrac{V_e^2}{c^2} - 1\right)\left(y\,\dfrac{V_i^2}{c^2} - 1\right)}{y\,\dfrac{V_s^2}{c^2} - 1} = \frac{\left(1 - \dfrac{y}{\epsilon_e}\right)\left(1 - \dfrac{y}{\epsilon_i}\right)}{1 - \dfrac{y}{\epsilon_s}} \qquad (8)$$

The dispersion curve is a hyperbola in the x-y plane. It is shown in Fig. 4.1 for $\epsilon_e = 10$, $m = 10$, and $\tau = \gamma_i T_i / Z\gamma_e T_e = 1$ (see Eq. 2.38). We have chosen for the ratio m a smaller value than encountered in reality in order to be able to show all the regions of the curve on the same scale. This curve has two asymptotes, one oblique and the other horizontal. The latter has an ordinate value

$$y = \epsilon_s = c^2/V_s^2 \qquad (9)$$

We shall later show that V_s may be considered to be the speed of sound in the plasma. Making use of the parameters m and τ, we can write the defining equations in the following ways

$$V_s^2 = (n_e m_e V_e^2 + n_i m_i V_i^2)/\rho = (mV_i^2 + V_e^2)/(m + 1)$$

$$= \frac{1 + \tau}{m + 1}\,V_e^2 = \frac{m}{m + 1}\frac{1 + \tau}{\tau}\,V_i^2 \simeq \frac{1 + \tau}{\tau}\,V_i^2 \qquad (10)$$

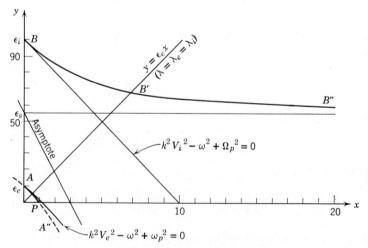

Fig. 4.1. Longitudinal waves ($m = 10$; $\tau = 1$; $\epsilon_e = 10$).

For the case where $\tau = 1$ we thus have

$$V_s^2 \simeq 2V_i^2 \tag{11}$$

The oblique asymptotes can be obtained from Eq. (8), giving

$$y + \left(\frac{\epsilon_e \epsilon_i}{\epsilon_s}\right) x = \epsilon_e + \epsilon_i - \epsilon_s \tag{12}$$

We can easily verify that, for $\tau = 1$, the orgin of the hyperbola is on the y axis, merely by noting that the asymptotes cross on that axis (see Fig. 4.1).

If we restrict ourselves to positive x and hence to that domain of the dispersion relation which has physical meaning, the two branches of the hyperbola reduce to the arcs APA'' and $BB'B''$. The tangents at A and B, respectively, are expressed by the equations

$$k^2 V_e^2 - \omega^2 + \omega_p^2 = 0 \tag{13}$$

$$k^2 V_i^2 - \omega^2 + \Omega_p^2 = 0 \tag{14}$$

These are parallel in the case $\tau = 1$.

The two arcs APA'' and $BB'B''$ correspond to two types of waves which differ in an important physical characteristic, to wit, the sign of the ratio v_{iz}/v_{ez}. By using Eq. (3) and observing the position of line $k^2 V_i^2 - \omega^2 + \Omega_p^2 = 0$ (the tangent at B), one sees that this ratio is negative for the arc APA'' and positive for $BB'B''$. For reasons which will be better understood in the light of the section following, we shall call the wave represented by the arc APA'' the electron wave and the one represented by $BB'B''$ the ion wave.

In the electron wave, the electron and ion oscillations are out of phase. In the ion wave they are in phase.

b. Ratio of electron-to-ion speeds. One calculates v_{ez} and v_{iz} as a function of E_z from Eqs. (2.24) and (2.24′).

$$v_{ez} = j\frac{q_e}{m_e \omega}\frac{\omega^2}{k^2 V_e^2 - \omega^2} E_z \tag{15}$$

$$v_{iz} = j\frac{q_i}{m_i \omega}\frac{\omega^2}{k^2 V_i^2 - \omega^2} E_z \tag{16}$$

The electron and ion speeds are 90° out of phase with the electric field. In addition, the points A and B in the dispersion curve give rise to singularities. At A the amplitude of the electron oscillations becomes infinite; the ion oscillations have similar behavior at B. Quite naturally, these results must be regarded with caution. They show that a linear theory of these phenomena is inadequate. We shall discuss this question in the section following in greater detail. First, however, we find it interesting to compare v_{ez} and v_{iz}. Equation (3) may be written

$$v_{iz}/v_{ez} = - (1/\tau) (y - \epsilon_e)/(y - \epsilon_i) \tag{17}$$

Figure 4.2 describes the behavior of this ratio for the same conditions as in Fig. 4.1. We shall discuss this figure in detail in later sections. However, we see immediately that the curves justify our labels for the two waves. In the electron wave, the ion oscillations are negligible; in the ion wave, the ion oscillations, on the contrary, dominate.*

We shall now study in greater detail each of these two waves by considering limiting cases. These cases have been treated extensively in the literature because of their importance and simplicity.

4.2   Electron Waves: Plasma Electron Oscillations

a. Ion motion. Figure 4.2 shows that the ions are essentially immobile in the electron wave. To establish this, note that along the arc AA', $v_\phi \gg V_i$ and $\omega \gg \Omega_p$, thus $k^2 V_i^2 - \omega^2 + \Omega_p^2 \cong - \omega^2$. Equation (3) now becomes

$$v_{iz}/v_{ez} \simeq - \omega_p^2/m\omega^2 = - \Omega_p^2/\omega^2 = - x/(m + 1) \tag{18}$$

This result approximates the slope of the tangent at A on fig. 4.2. One sees that the amplitude of the ion motion is inversely propor-

---

*We shall see in Chapter 6, Eq. (6.5), that the ratios v_{iz}/v_{ez} for the electron mode and v_{iz}'/v_{ez}' for the ion mode satisfy the relation

$$\frac{v_{iz}}{v_{ez}} \frac{v_{iz}'}{v_{ez}'} = - 1/\tau$$

tional to the square of the frequency. Finally, one verifies anew that
in the electron wave electrons and ions oscillate in opposite phase.

b. Dispersion relation. If we set $y = 0$ in Eq. (8), the result
is $x = 1$. The dispersion curve thus intersects the x axis at P, corresponding to the critical frequency

$$\omega = \omega_0 = (\omega_p^2 + \Omega_p^2)^{1/2} \tag{19}$$

The tangent at A given by Eq. (13) intersects the x axis at the point
A' where $\omega = \omega_p$. The points A' and P are nearly identical. The

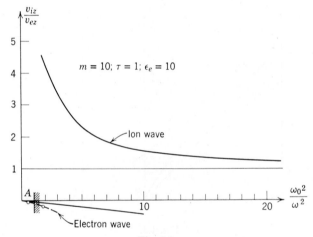

Fig. 4.2.

dispersion curve from A to P lies between the cord AP and its
tangent AA' at A. Hence we may, without any appreciable error,
replace the dispersion relation by the equation of either of these
two lines which coincide in the limit of infinite ion mass. In the
latter case Ω_p and the ion motion would be exactly zero, and the
dispersion relation for electron waves would be Eq. (13).

We shall replace the dispersion curve between the points A and
P by the cord AP (see Fig. 4.3). The exact dispersion relation
Eq. (4), is thus replaced by the approximate relation Eq. (20) or
Eq. (21).

$$k^2 V_e^2 - \omega^2 + \omega_0^2 = 0 \tag{20}$$

$$(y/\epsilon_e) + x - 1 = 0 \tag{21}$$

When the thermal speed V_e is zero, Eq. (20) reduces to Eq. (19). The plasma can support oscillations of frequency ω_0, but these are stationary oscillations; their group velocity v_g is zero. In addition, we can observe that the effect of the ions is to increase the apparent "stiffness" of the medium; the characteristic frequency is slightly larger than the electron plasma frequency.

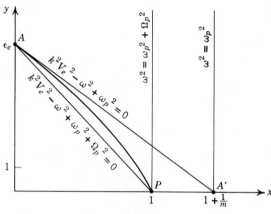

Fig. 4.3.

If V_e is not zero, the dispersion relation shows that the frequency ω_0 plays the role of a critical frequency for longitudinal waves as well as for transverse waves. The waves of frequency below ω_0 are evanescent.

To aid our discussion of the dispersion relation, we introduce a characteristic length for electron waves

$$\lambda_e = 2\pi V_e/\omega_0 \simeq 2\pi \gamma_e^{1/2} h_e \tag{22}$$

where h_e is the Debye length, defined by

$$h_e^2 = KT_e/4\pi \bar{n}_e q_e^2 c^2 \tag{23}$$

For $\gamma_e = 3$ the result is $\lambda_e = 10.9\ h_e$. The ratio of the wave length to the characteristic length can be expressed in the form

$$\lambda/\lambda_e = \omega_0/kV_e = (\epsilon_e x/y)^{1/2} = [x/(1-x)]^{1/2} \qquad (24)$$

Figure 4.4 shows the variation of this ratio as a function of x; the wave length goes to zero as the frequency becomes infinite and to infinity when the frequency approaches the plasma frequency. For values of x larger than 0.5, the wave length is greater than the Debye length by factors larger than 10.

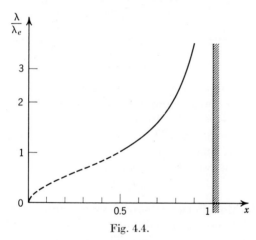

Fig. 4.4.

c. Phase and group velocities. Waves of frequency $\omega > \omega_0$ propagate with the phase velocity v_ϕ given by

$$v_\phi = \left(V_e^2 + \frac{\omega_0^2}{k^2}\right)^{1/2} = V_e \left(1 + \frac{\lambda^2}{\lambda_e^2}\right)^{1/2} \qquad (25)$$

that is

$$v_\phi = V_e \left(1 + \frac{x}{1-x}\right)^{1/2} = \frac{V_e}{(1-x)^{1/2}} \qquad (26)$$

The group velocity is

$$v_g = \mathbf{d}\omega/\mathbf{d}k = k/\omega\ V_e^2 = V_e(1-x)^{1/2} \qquad (27)$$

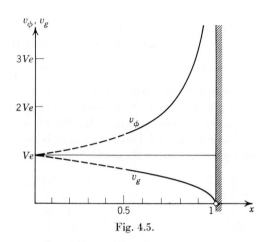

Fig. 4.5.

Figure 4.5 shows the variation of v_ϕ and v_g as a function of x. The speed v_ϕ is always larger than V_e, "the speed of sound in the electron gas." This is due to the resonance of the plasma at the critical plasma frequency. The group velocity is, on the other hand, smaller than V_e and approaches zero as the critical frequency is approached. The two speeds, v_ϕ and v_g, are related by

$$v_\phi v_g = V_e^2 \tag{28}$$

d. Distinction between sound waves and plasma oscillations. It is interesting to meditate somewhat on the mechanism of excitation of waves in a plasma. There exists a fundamental difference between the nature of the sound waves that propagate in a neutral gas and the plasma waves that propagate in a gas of charged particles. This difference stems from the range of interaction of the forces involved. The two media establish the coherent movement of particles (from which there results a wave) in a different manner. In both cases every particle is tied to the motion of the aggregate by interactions with the others. Whereas the range of forces between neutrals is generally smaller than the interparticle distance, the range of forces between charges is limited only by the Debye length, which, in general, is considerably larger than the average particle separation.

In the first case it is the multiplicity of short range, nearly incoherent collisions undergone by each particle which transfers to it a certain average momentum parallel to the motion of the ensemble. In the charged particle case, short-range encounters are of a secondary importance and could even be neglected. Most of the momentum is transferred to each particle by a large number of distant charges contained in a volume of dimensions of order of the Debye length. Through the coupling provided by the electric field, these interactions result in a coherent disturbance which is described by the Poisson equation. Hence a term in ω_0^2, which simply expresses the fact that a plasma possesses a characteristic frequency of vibration. A neutral gas has no such property.

e. Microscopic analysis of plasma oscillations. We shall now describe an analysis due to Bohm and Gross [10] which will clarify the mechanism by which a plasma can support and propagate oscillations. A longitudinal plane wave can be described by the variations of the potential $\phi(z)$ as a function of z. The minima of the potential correspond to regions of electron density larger than the average and conversely. The orientation of the electric field resulting from this distribution is shown in Fig. 4.6. Let us consider

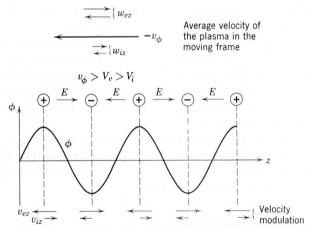

Fig. 4.6. Detailed structure of plasma oscillations.

a frame of reference tied to the wave. In this frame the potential curve $\phi(z)$ is stationary, and it is the body of the plasma which is moving with a mass velocity, $-v_\phi$, which is in the direction opposite to the wave. If w_{ez} is the average z component of the velocity of a given electron in the laboratory system, its average velocity component in the frame moving with the wave is $w_{ez} - v_\phi$.

If $v_\phi > V_e$, the speed $w_{ez} - v_\phi$ is generally negative, and we have for a majority of electrons

$$\tfrac{1}{2}\, m_e(w_{ez} - v_\phi)^2 > q_e\phi_m \qquad (29)$$

if the amplitude ϕ_m of the potential wave is small. We can see that the electrons under the influence of the field **E** of the wave are simply slowed down during their traversal of the minima of the potential and accelerated in the neighborhood of the maxima. Statistically, therefore, the electrons have a tendency to accumulate in the regions where they already are in excess. This modulation of the velocity results in the ability to support the wave, and the effect is stronger and more effective when the velocity of the electrons relative to the wave is small. Consequently, the wave will be principally supported by these electrons whose thermal velocity is in the same direction as the wave velocity. We now understand how under these conditions the wave, once excited, continues to propagate in the same direction.

However, those electrons whose speed w_{ez} is sufficiently close to that of the wave and who do not satisfy the inequality, Eq. (29), cannot go beyond the minima in the potential. They remain trapped in the maxima and serve to reduce the amplitude of the wave. The number of these trapped electrons becomes larger as the wave velocity v_ϕ approaches V_e.

Some authors [12] think that this effect is equivalent to the attenuation mechanism initially predicted by Landau [11]. In any case, various theories [13] show that only waves of velocity v_ϕ much larger than V_e can propagate.*

---

*A similar attenuation mechanism exists for transverse waves in the neighborhood of the electron cyclotron frequency [23, 24].

If we accept, as the various aforementioned theories seem to demonstrate, that, to propagate, the waves must satisfy

$$v_\phi > (2)^{1/2} V_e \tag{30}$$

we find, from Eq. (25), the following condition for the wave length of those oscillations that can be propagated

$$\lambda > \lambda_e \tag{31}$$

For this reason we have indicated in Figs. 4.4 and 4.5 the sections of the curve, located on the left, by dashed lines.

4.3 Ion Waves: Ion Oscillations in a Plasma and Pseudosonic Waves

For the ion wave, shown by the upper branch in Fig. 4.1,

$$V_i < v_\phi < V_s \tag{32}$$

On the other hand, the electron temperature is, in most cases equal to or larger than the ion temperature. Consequently, $\tau \leq 1$, and, from Eq. (10), V_s is much smaller than V_e, giving

$$v_\phi \ll V_e \tag{33}$$

The phase velocity of ion waves is always well below V_e. Thus

$$k^2 V_e^2 \gg \omega^2 \tag{34}$$

This inequality enables us to replace the dispersion relation, Eq. (4), by an approximate expression. This simplification will be carried out in a different manner in the two wave length regions on both sides of the critical electron wave length λ_e. We shall differentiate the two cases:

1. For $\lambda \ll \lambda_e$ we have ion plasma oscillations in which $v_{iz} \gg v_{ez}$.
2. For $\lambda \gg \lambda_e$ we have pseudosonic waves in which $v_{iz} \simeq v_{ez}$.

a. Oscillation of ions in a plasma. Let us assume first that

$$\lambda \ll \lambda_e \tag{35}$$

and

$$k^2 V_e^2 \gg \omega_p^2 \qquad (36)$$

1. *Electron motion.* From Eq. (3) we then have

$$v_{iz}/v_{ez} \simeq k^2 V_e^2/m\Omega_p^2 = k^2 V_e^2/\omega_p^2 \simeq \lambda_e^2/\lambda^2 \qquad (37)$$

The ion velocity is much larger than that of the electrons, the ratio being inverse to the square of the wave length.

2. *Approximate dispersion relation.* The two inequalities, Eqs. (34) and (36), allow us to write the dispersion relation, Eq. (4), in the approximate form

$$k^2 V_i^2 - \omega^2 + \Omega_p^2 = \omega_p^2 \Omega_p^2/k^2 V_e^2 \qquad (38)$$

or, essentially,

$$k^2 V_i^2 - \omega^2 + \Omega_p^2 = 0 \qquad (39)$$

In this last form we see that our approximations result in reducing the dispersion curve to the line which forms its tangent at B. Equation (39) is completely similar to that describing the electron oscillations. We can formally obtain expressions for the wave length and the phase and group velocities of this wave by replacing the electron parameters in the appropriate formulas by ion parameters and ω_0 by Ω_p. In particular, we may define a critical wave length for ion oscillations

$$\lambda_i = 2\pi V_i/\Omega_p = \lambda_e \tau^{1/2} \qquad (40)$$

and we obtain

$$v_\phi = V_i[1 + (\lambda^2/\lambda_i^2)]^{1/2} \qquad (41)$$

b. Conditions for the existence of ion oscillations in a plasma. In order that the range of validity of Eq. (39) be large, it is necessary that the tangent to the hyperbola at B should remain close to the curve over a large interval. In other words we require that the slope, $\epsilon_e \epsilon_i/\epsilon_s$, of the asymptote be in the neighborhood of $\epsilon_i/(m+1)$, the slope of the tangent at B. By making use of Eq. (10), this condition is written

$$\tau \ll 1 \qquad (42)$$

For example, Fig. 4.7 shows the dispersion curve for the ion mode for $m = 10$, $\epsilon_e = 10$, $\epsilon_i = 10^4$, and therefore $\tau = 10^{-2}$. The physical meaning of Eq. (42) is clear enough. It asserts that the thermal speeds of the electrons are much larger than those of the ions. Electrons do not feel the ion oscillations because they move too rapidly.

A microscopic analysis, analogous to that made for the electron oscillations, requires us to consider Eq. (42) as the condition for the existence of ion oscillations in a plasma. In fact, if we say, as previously, that the condition for ion wave propagation is

$$v_\phi > (2)^{1/2} V_i \tag{43}$$

we are led to the condition

$$\lambda > \lambda_i = \lambda_e \tau^{1/2} \tag{44}$$

The inequalities Eqs. (35) and (44) can only be compatible if τ is much smaller than unity. We can construct this result graphically from Figs. 4.1 and 4.7 by drawing on these figures the line $\lambda = \lambda_e$ and $\lambda = \lambda_i$. Ion plasma waves exist in the region included between

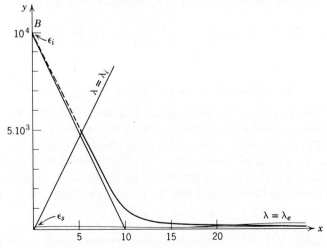

Fig. 4.7. Dispersion curve of the ion mode ($\epsilon_e = 10$; $\epsilon_i = 10^4$; $m = 10$).

those lines. In Fig. 4.1 these lines coincide. On the other hand, when $\tau \ll 1$, the region between the lines, in which ion plasma waves can exist, is large. Therefore it is only under rather severe and unusual conditions ($Z\gamma_e T_e \gg \gamma_i T_i$) that ion plasma oscillations can be excited.

c. Pseudosonic waves. The dispersion curve in Fig. 4.1 shows a horizontal asymptote for the ion wave which we have already mentioned several times. This means that in the region of low frequencies v_ϕ becomes independent of frequency; there is no dispersion. In this same region we have $v_{ez} \simeq v_{iz}$. The electrons and ions move together. These two properties make the low frequency ion waves resemble sound waves. We have therefore given them the name "pseudosonic waves."

1. Phase velocity. Now let us assume

$$\lambda \gg \lambda_e \tag{45}$$

or

$$k^2 V_e{}^2 \ll \omega_p{}^2$$

If, in addition, we assume $\omega \ll \omega_p$, we can write Eq. (4) as

$$k^2 V_i{}^2 - \omega^2 + \Omega_p{}^2 = \frac{\omega_p{}^2 \Omega_p{}^2}{\omega_p{}^2 + k^2 V_e{}^2} \simeq \Omega_p{}^2 \left(1 - \frac{k^2 V_e{}^2}{\omega^2}\right) \tag{46}$$

or

$$\omega^2 = k^2(\omega_p{}^2 V_i{}^2 + \Omega_p{}^2 V_e{}^2)/(\omega_p{}^2 + \Omega_p{}^2) = k^2 V_s{}^2 \tag{47}$$

Thus, we recover the phase speed V_s given by Eq. (6). We shall henceforth call this speed the "sound speed in a plasma." The speed V_s is, in gneral, of the order of V_i; if the electron temperature were zero, V_s would, of course, equal V_i. The thermal motion of the electrons has the effect of increasing V_s. In the more common case of a plasma in thermal equilibrium ($\gamma_i = \gamma_e$), we have

$$V_s = (1 + Z)^{1/2} V_i \tag{48}$$

Finally, if $T_e \gg T_i$, the sound speed is considerably larger than V_i. These conditions are described in Fig. 4.7.

2. *Space charge in pseudosonic waves.* For ion waves the electron and ion velocities are in phase, and v_{iz}/v_{ez} tends toward unity as x becomes infinite. For very low frequencies the electrons accompany the ions in their motion, and the medium remains practically neutral. However, this is only rigorously true for infinite x. For finite values of x (or of the frequency) there exists a slight deviation from neutrality; the ion oscillations are slightly larger than those of the electrons. Using Eq. (3) and the approximate dispersion relation, Eq. (46), we obtain

$$v_{iz}/v_{ez} \simeq 1 + (k^2 V_e^2/\omega_p^2) = 1 + (\lambda_e^2/\lambda^2) \qquad (49)$$

Whence, according to Eqs. (2.18) and (2.19),

$$n_e = \bar{n}_e v_{ez}/v_\phi \qquad (50)$$

$$n_i = \bar{n}_i v_{iz}/v_\phi \qquad (51)$$

$$n_e + n_i \simeq (\bar{n}_e + \bar{n}_i)v_{ez}/V_s \qquad (52)$$

The amplitude of this oscillation of the total density is proportional to v_{ez}, the amplitude of the electron velocity oscillation. Similarly, the residual space charge is given by

$$n_e q_e + n_i q_i = \bar{n}_e q_e \frac{v_{ez}}{v_\phi} \left(1 + \frac{\bar{n}_i q_i}{\bar{n}_e q_e} \frac{v_{iz}}{v_{ez}} \right) \simeq - \bar{n}_e q_e \frac{v_{ez}}{V_s} \frac{\lambda_e^2}{\lambda^2} \qquad (53)$$

Pseudosonic waves differ from ordinary sound waves only by this deviation from neutrality, which is proportional to the amplitude of the electron velocity oscillation and to the square of the frequency. Even though this deviation is weak, an electric field resulting from the space charge produces a coupling between the aggregate motion of electrons and ions. The motion of the plasma is analogous to ambipolar diffusion; the effectiveness of coulomb interactions is such that we need only a very small deviation from neutrality to insure a complete coupling between the two species of particles.

Figure 4.8 summarizes the properties of pseudosonic waves. This diagram can be considered as demonstrating the phenomena either in the laboratory system or in the frame of the wave. In the

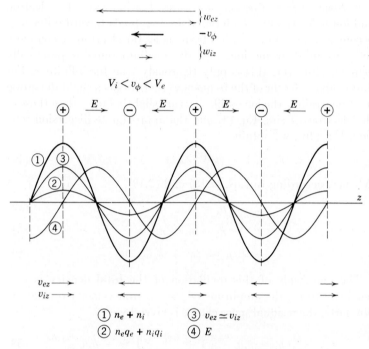

Fig. 4.8. Detailed structure of pseudosonic waves.

latter case we can consider, as previously, that the plasma is moving with an aggregate velocity, $-v_\phi$, which is superimposed on the thermal motion. This is shown in Fig. 4.8 by the quantities ω_{ez} and ω_{iz}.

CHAPTER 5

Classification of Waves and Plasmas

5.1 Transfer of Energy in a Wave*

a. The various forms of the energy. The energy contained in a unit volume of plasma can be considered as the sum of four terms:

1. The electrical energy:

$$W_E = E^2/8\pi c^2 \tag{1}$$

2. The magnetic energy:

$$W_M = B^2/8\pi \tag{2}$$

3. The kinetic energy:

$$W_K = \tfrac{1}{2}\bar{n}_e m_e \mathbf{v}_e^2 + \tfrac{1}{2}\bar{n}_i m_i \mathbf{v}_i^2 \tag{3}$$

4. The potential energy:

$$W_P = \tfrac{1}{2}\bar{n}_e m_e V_e^2 (\mathrm{n}_e/\bar{n}_e)^2 + \tfrac{1}{2}\bar{n}_i m_i V_i^2 (\mathrm{n}_i/\bar{n}_i)^2 \tag{4}$$

The first three definitions need no comment. The last relates to the classical ideas of fluid dynamics [14] in the following way. Let us define the coefficient of compressiblity χ_e of the electron fluid by

$$\mathrm{p}_e = \chi_e \mathrm{n}_e/\bar{n}_e \tag{5}$$

which, with the aid of Eq. (1.25), becomes

---

*In this chapter, as in Chapters 1 and 2, do not confuse the instantaneous magnitudes (functions of time and space) written in Roman characters with the complex amplitudes in a wave written in italicized characters.

$$\chi_e = \bar{n}_e m_e V_e^2 \tag{6}$$

This allows us to express the potential energy of the electrons as

$$W_{Pe} = \tfrac{1}{2}(p_e^2/\chi_e) = \tfrac{1}{2}\bar{n}_e m_e V_e^2 (n_e/\bar{n}_e)^2 \tag{7}$$

By doing the same computation for the ions and summing, we obtain definition (4).

b. Equation for electromagnetic energy transfer. We can easily obtain the transport equation for electromagnetic energy. For this, it suffices to combine Eqs. (1.14) and (1.16). By scalar multiplying the first by **B** and the second by $-$**E** and adding, we obtain the equation

$$\mathbf{B}\cdot(\boldsymbol{\nabla}\times\mathbf{E}) - \mathbf{E}\cdot(\boldsymbol{\nabla}\times\mathbf{B}) = -4\pi\mathbf{E}\cdot\mathbf{J} - \tfrac{1}{2}\frac{\partial}{\partial t}\left(\frac{\mathrm{E}^2}{c^2} + \mathrm{B}^2\right) \tag{8}$$

or using the vector identity

$$\boldsymbol{\nabla}\cdot(\mathbf{E}\times\mathbf{B}) = \mathbf{B}\cdot(\boldsymbol{\nabla}\times\mathbf{E}) - \mathbf{E}\cdot(\boldsymbol{\nabla}\times\mathbf{B}) \tag{9}$$

we arrive at

$$\boldsymbol{\nabla}\cdot\mathbf{N} + \mathbf{E}\cdot\mathbf{J} = -(\partial/\partial t)(W_E + W_M) \tag{10}$$

by introducing the Poynting vector (flux of electromagnetic energy) which is

$$\mathbf{N} = (\mathbf{E}\times\mathbf{B})/4\pi \tag{11}$$

Equation (10) ascribes the reduction of the electromagnetic energy $W_E + W_M$ enclosed in a small volume element to the divergence of **N** (radiated flux) and to the work done by the electric field. This equation is valid at any instant; **E, B**, and **J** are instantaneous values. As this equation is in direct consequence of Maxwell's equations, it is automatically satisfied in all cases.

c. Equation for mechanical energy transfer. It is impossible for us to study correctly the transfer of "caloric" energy associated with the wave because we have ignored the transfer equation for kinetic pressure. On this subject, we were satisfied by the more or less vulnerable adiabaticity conditions, (Eqs. 1.25) and (1.26). Whenever these conditions are valid, we can deduce linearized equations for the exchange of momentum and an approximate equation for the transfer of mechanical energy. For this purpose we multiply Eq. (1.20) by $\mathbf{v}_e$ and Eq. (1.21) by $\mathbf{v}_i$. Setting $\nu = \nu_{en} = \nu_{in} = 0$, we obtain

$$(\partial/\partial t)\ (\tfrac{1}{2}\bar{n}_e m_e \mathbf{v}_e^2) = \bar{n}_e q_e \mathbf{v}_e \cdot \mathbf{E} - \mathbf{v}_e \cdot \nabla \mathrm{p}_e \tag{12}$$

and

$$(\partial/\partial t)\ (\tfrac{1}{2}\bar{n}_i m_i \mathbf{v}_i^2) = \bar{n}_i q_i \mathbf{v}_i \cdot \mathbf{E} - \mathbf{v}_i \cdot \nabla \mathrm{p}_i \tag{13}$$

Adding these equations,

$$(\partial \mathrm{W}_K / \partial t) = \mathbf{E} \cdot \mathbf{J} - \mathrm{P} \tag{14}$$

or

$$\mathrm{P} = \mathbf{v}_e \cdot \nabla \mathrm{p}_e + \mathbf{v}_i \cdot \nabla \mathrm{p}_i \tag{15}$$

This is the work done by the pressure of an element on its neighboring element.

We can transform the expression for P, following Field [22], by first making use of Eqs. (1.25) and (1.26). We obtain

$$\mathrm{P} = m_e V_e^2 \mathbf{v}_e \cdot \nabla \mathrm{n}_e + m_i V_i^2 \mathbf{v}_i \cdot \nabla \mathrm{n}_i \tag{16}$$

which becomes, in virtue of the identity $\nabla \cdot n\mathbf{v} = n \nabla \cdot \mathbf{v} + \mathbf{v} \cdot \nabla n$,

$$\mathrm{P} = m_e V_e^2 \nabla \cdot \mathrm{n}_e \mathbf{v}_e + m_i V_i^2 \nabla \cdot \mathrm{n}_i \mathbf{v}_i$$

$$- m_e V_e^2 \mathrm{n}_e \nabla \cdot \mathbf{v}_e - m_i V_i^2 \mathrm{n}_i \nabla \cdot \mathbf{v}_i. \tag{17}$$

Also, the conservation equation (1.18) allows us to write

$$\mathrm{n}_e \nabla \cdot \mathbf{v}_e = \frac{\mathrm{n}_e}{\bar{n}_e} \nabla \cdot \bar{n}_e \mathbf{v}_e = - \frac{\mathrm{n}_e}{\bar{n}_e} \frac{\partial \mathrm{n}_e}{\partial t} = - \tfrac{1}{2} \bar{n}_e \frac{\partial}{\partial t} \left(\frac{\mathrm{n}_e}{\bar{n}_e} \right)^2 \tag{18}$$

and, consequently,

$$\mathrm{P} = \nabla \cdot (\mathrm{n}_e m_e V_e^2 \mathbf{v}_e + \mathrm{n}_i m_i V_i^2 \mathbf{v}_i) + (\partial/\partial t)\ \mathrm{W}_P \tag{19}$$

Equation (14) thus leads us to the relation

$$\nabla \cdot \mathbf{N}' - \mathbf{E} \cdot \mathbf{J} = - (\partial/\partial t)\ (\mathrm{W}_K + \mathrm{W}_P) \tag{20}$$

where we have introduced the vector

$$\mathbf{N'} = n_e m_e V_e^2 \mathbf{v}_e + n_i m_i V_i^2 \mathbf{v}_i \qquad (21)$$

The vector $\mathbf{N'}$ can be considered as the energy flux carried by the particles.

Combining Eqs. (10) and (20), we can eliminate the term $\mathbf{E} \cdot \mathbf{J}$, which is the energy given to the plasma by the field, and write the transport equation for total energy:

$$\nabla \cdot (\mathbf{N} + \mathbf{N'}) + (\partial/\partial t)(W_E + W_M + W_K + W_P) = 0 \quad (22)$$

This equation expresses the decrease in the local energy in the plasma, existing in electrical, magnetic, kinetic, or potential form, as being equal to the divergence of the energy flux carried by electromagnetic radiation and by the thermal energy of the particles.

5.2 The Relation of Various Forms of Energy

Equation (22) stems directly from Maxwell's equations and the equations of conservation; it is valid for any type of perturbation. We may now specialize to the case of a monochromatic plane wave propagating in the z direction, and then invoke Eqs. (2.10) and (2.11), which relate the amplitudes of the electric and magnetic fields of the wave ($\mathbf{E}$ and $\mathbf{B}$), and Eqs. (2.18) and (2.19), which relate the amplitudes of the densities n_e and n_i to the velocities $\mathbf{v}_e$ and $\mathbf{v}_i$.

$$\left.\begin{aligned}
\nabla \cdot \mathbf{N} &= \frac{\partial}{\partial z} \frac{E_x^2 + E_y^2}{4\pi v_\phi} = 2v_\phi \frac{\partial}{\partial z} \frac{B_x^2 + B_y^2}{8\pi} = 2v_\phi \frac{\partial}{\partial z} W_M \\
\nabla \cdot \mathbf{N'} &= \frac{\partial}{\partial z} \frac{\bar{n}_e m_e V_e^2 \mathbf{v}_{ez}^2 + \bar{n}_i m_i V_i^2 \mathbf{v}_{iz}^2}{v_\phi} \\
&= 2v_\phi \frac{\partial}{\partial z}\left[\tfrac{1}{2}\bar{n}_e m_e V_e^2 \left(\frac{n_e}{\bar{n}_e}\right)^2 + \tfrac{1}{2}\bar{n}_i m_i V_i^2 \left(\frac{n_i}{\bar{n}_i}\right)^2\right] \\
&= 2v_\phi \frac{\partial}{\partial z} W_P
\end{aligned}\right\} \quad (23)$$

In cases of interest, W is proportional to $\cos^2 (\omega t - kz + \phi)$, and thus

$$\partial W/\partial z = - (k/w) (\partial W/\partial t) = - (1/v_\phi) (\partial W/\partial t)$$

We obtain

$$\boldsymbol{\nabla} \cdot (\mathbf{N} + \mathbf{N}') = - 2 (\partial/\partial t) (W_M + W_P) \qquad (24)$$

By combining Eqs. (22) and (24),

$$(\partial/\partial t) (W_E - W_M + W_K - W_P) = 0$$

from which we deduce the basic relation

$$(W_M + W_P) - (W_E + W_K) = \text{Constant} \qquad (25)$$

The constant in Eq. (25) is zero for certain simple cases where the energy terms have a time variation proportional to $\cos^2 (\omega t - kz + \phi)$. This happens when all the variables are in phase.

There exist two well-known special cases of this relation. For electromagnetic waves in a vacuum, $W_K = W_P = 0$, and the electric and magnetic energies are always equal. In the case of sound waves in a neutral gas, $W_M = W_E = 0$, and the kinetic and potential energies are equal.

As has been shown by Van de Hulst [6], this constant is also zero in the case of magnetodynamic waves for which

$$W_M + W_P = W_E + W_K$$

Finally, Eq. (23) allows the calculation of the time average of the total energy transported by the wave in the z direction.

$$\overline{N}_z + \overline{N}'_z = \left(\frac{E_x^2 + E_y^2}{8\pi c^2} \right) \frac{c^2}{v_\phi} + (\tfrac{1}{2}\bar{n}_e m_e v_{ez}^2) \frac{V_e^2}{v_\phi} \\ + (\tfrac{1}{2}\bar{n}_i m_i v_{iz}^2) \frac{V_i^2}{v_\phi} \qquad (26)$$

The direction of propagation of the total energy carried by the wave is given by the vector

$$\mathbf{N} + \mathbf{N}' = (\mathbf{E} \times \mathbf{B})/4\pi + n_e m_e V_e^2 \mathbf{v}_e + n_i m_i V_i^2 \mathbf{v}_i$$

This direction is, in general, not the z direction; it is not perpendicular to the plane of the wave.

5.3 Some Comments about Transverse and Longitudinal Waves

The conservation equation (22) shows that an essential difference exists between the transverse and longitudinal waves.

For transverse waves, $\mathbf{N}' = 0$, and only a flux of electromagnetic energy is necessary to insure propagation. For longitudinal waves, $\mathbf{N} = 0$, and only the flux of mechanical energy comes into the picture.

For transverse "electromagnetic" waves, $W_P = 0$. The plasma plays only an auxiliary role in the propagation of the waves; the only effect of the particle current is to alter the propagation constant. The plasma behaves as a dielectric, and waves of this type can exist outside of the plasma, where they are ordinary electromagnetic waves.

For "acoustical" longitudinal waves, $W_M = 0$. Here the plasma plays an essential role. The plasma provides support for the wave whose propagation is connected to the energy transport of the particles. This type of wave cannot exist outside of a plasma.

We can note that the $\mathbf{E} \cdot \mathbf{J}$ term, which is the energy exchanged from the fields to the particles, drops out of Eq. (22). In purely transverse or longitudinal waves, this term represents the coupling between the electrical energy W_E and the kinetic energy W_K. Even if the exchange between these two forms of energy does not play an essential role in the mechanism of propagation, in practice it has an important influence on the structure of the waves.

In fact, it is the exchange of energy between the transverse components of the electric field and the particle velocities which gives us resonances at the gyromagnetic frequency ω_L and Ω_L. Similarly, it is the energy exchange between the longitudinal components of the electric field and the velocities which leads to the self-oscillation of the plasma at the frequency w_0. As we know, these phenomena of resonance and oscillatory behavior are very important in determining the form of the dispersion curves.

When there exists a transverse component of the macroscopic magnetic field, the $\mathbf{E} \cdot \mathbf{J}$ term also represents a coupling between the magnetic and potential energies; the mechanisms for electromagnetic and acoustical propagation are together associated with the propagation of the wave. The nature of this coupling then depends on the relative magnitudes of ω_L, Ω_L, and ω_0, as we shall now see.

5.4 Classification of Plasmas

The preceding development enables us to classify plasmas using, as a basis, the following three remarks:

1. The parameter A is a measure of the plasma density compared to the intensity of the magnetic field. More exactly, we note that the perturbations caused by the plasma on the propagation of transverse electromagnetic waves and, in particular, on the conduction current, are proportional to A. The result can be verified with the use of Fig. 3.2.

a. For $A < 1$ the index of refraction for transverse waves is always in the neighborhood of unity, except in the immediate neighborhood of the gyromagnetic resonances. In this case we call the plasma rarified (and also very rarified, see below).

b. For $A > 1$ the index is always different from unity; the plasma has a strong influence on the propagation of electromagnetic waves even outside of the resonances. We then call the plasma dense (and also moderately dense, see below).

2. The sequence of magnitudes of the three fundamental frequencies ω_0, ω_b, and Ω_b determines the nature of coupling between transverse and longitudinal waves.

The condition $A = 1$, which separates rarified from dense plasmas, is equivalent to

$$\omega_0 = \sqrt{\omega_b \Omega_b}$$

The relative magnitude of ω_0 compared to the two gyromagnetic frequencies allows us to subdivide the above two groups as follows:

a. Very rarified plasmas $\omega_0 < \Omega_b$ $\left(A < \dfrac{1}{m}\right)$

b. Rarified plasmas $\Omega_b < \omega_0 < \sqrt{\omega_b \Omega_b}$ $\left(\dfrac{1}{m} < A < 1\right)$

c. Moderately dense plasmas $\sqrt{\omega_b \Omega_b} < \omega_0 < \omega_b$ $(1 < A < m)$

d. Dense plasmas $\omega_b < \omega_0$ $(m < A)$

3. The relative magnitudes of V_a and V_s modify the nature of the coupling in dense plasmas. In fact, the coupling between the longitudinal and transverse waves, which is introduced by the transverse component B_T, occurs whenever the phase velocity of the two types of waves are equal; these are the points of congruence of their dispersion curves.

As we shall see in greater detail in Chapter 6, the number of real meeting points depends more on the relative position of the horizontal asymptotes of the two curves $y = \epsilon_s$ and $y = 1 + A = \epsilon_a$ than on the order in which ω_0, ω_b, and Ω_b occur. Let us now consider the condition $V_a = V_s$. According to Eqs. (3.24) and (4.10), we obtain, letting $\omega_p \approx \omega_0$

$$(c^2/m)\,(\omega_b{}^2/\omega_0{}^2) = mV_i{}^2 + V_e{}^2/(m+1) \qquad (27)$$

from which we deduce

$$B_0{}^2/4\pi \simeq \gamma_e \bar{n}_e K T_e + \gamma_i \bar{n}_i K T_i \qquad (28)$$

The magnetic pressure $B_0{}^2/8\pi$ is of the same order of magnitude as the kinetic pressure $\bar{n}_e K T_e + \bar{n}_i K T_i$ in this instance. We also find this criterion when we consider the possibility of "confining" a plasma by means of a magnetic field in a limited volume [15]. Therefore we label as

a. Confined plasmas, plasmas for which $V_s < V_a$
b. Unconfined plasmas, plasmas for which $V_s > V_a$

We easily verify that the separation between these two groups is found in the region of plasmas which we have called very dense.

We write Eq. (27) as

$$\omega_0{}^2/\omega_b{}^2 \simeq c^2/(V_e{}^2 + m V_i{}^2) = c^2/V_e{}^2(1 + \tau) \qquad (29)$$

This last ratio is, in general, greater than unity.

The above considerations lead to a classification as shown in Table 5.1. The plasmas are classified in order of increasing density (and/or decreasing magnetic field). We have indicated the critical values of ω_0, A, and of $\bar{n}_e/B_0{}^2$ which separate the different categories of plasma. The labeling is related to the fact that the plasmas

Table 5.1

ω_0	Ω_b	$\sqrt{\omega_b \Omega_b}$	ω_b	
A	$\dfrac{1}{m}$	1	m	$\dfrac{6 \times 10^9\, m}{\gamma_e T_e(1 + \tau)}$
$\dfrac{\bar{n}_e}{B_0{}^2}$	$\dfrac{10^5}{m^2}$	$\dfrac{10^5}{m}$	10^5	$\dfrac{6 \times 10^{14}}{\gamma_e T_e(1 + \tau)}$
V_s				V_a
Plasmas	Very rarified	Rarified	Moderately dense	Dense
				Confined $V_s < V_a$ / Unconfined $V_s > V_a$

of the first two groups correspond, in practice, to very rarified gases placed in a strong magnetic field. The usual plasmas (discharges or astrophysical plasmas, as in Table 3.1) are the dense or moderately dense plasmas. The domains in which these five types of plasma exist are also shown in Fig. 5.1, in which the ordinate is the temperature and the abscissa the value of the ratio $\bar{n}_e/B_0{}^2$. The numerical values shown have been computed for a plasma of electrons and protons ($m = 1836$); for the sake of simplicity, we have assumed that $T_e = T_i = T$.

Table 5.2

Representative plasmas

	Parameters	P_1	P_2	P_3	P_4	P_5
Fundamental parameters	A	10^{-5}	10^{-2}	10^2	10^6	10^{10}
	ϵ_a	1	1.01	1.01×10^2	10^6	10^{10}
	ϵ_s	10^8	10^8	10^8	10^8	10^8
	ϵ_e	1.09×10^5	1.09×10^5	1.09×10^5	1.09×10^5	1.09×10^5
	ϵ_i	2×10^8	2×10^8	2×10^8	2×10^8	2×10^8
Various physical parameters	$\bar{n}_e/B_0^2$	5.5×10^{-4}	5.5×10^{-1}	5.5×10^3	5.5×10^7	5.5×10^{11}
	ω_p/ω_b	7.3×10^{-5}	2.3×10^{-3}	2.3×10^{-1}	2.3×10^1	2.3×10^3
	Ω_p/Ω_b	3.2×10^{-3}	10^{-1}	10	10^3	10^5
	V_a	3×10^{10}	3×10^{10}	3×10^9	3×10^7	3×10^5
	V_s	3×10^6	3×10^6	3×10^6	3×10^6	3×10^6
	V_e	9.1×10^7	9.1×10^7	9.1×10^7	9.1×10^7	9.1×10^7
	V_i	2.1×10^6	2.1×10^6	2.1×10^6	2.1×10^6	2.1×10^6
Examples	$T(\gamma_e = \gamma_i = 3)$	1.85×10^1	1.85×10^4	1.85×10^4	1.85×10^4	1.85×10^4
	$\bar{n}_e$	5.5×10^4	5.5×10^7	5.5×10^{11}	5.5×10^{15}	5.5×10^{19}
	B_0	10^4	10^4	10^4	10^4	10^4

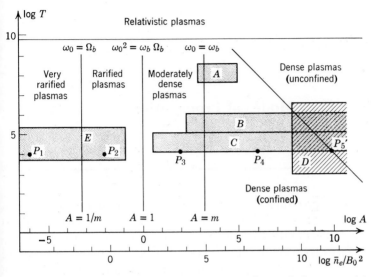

Fig. 5.1. Plasma groups. P_1, P_2, P_3, P_4, and P_5 are five typical cases used in numerical computations.

A = Future thermonuclear reactors ( ).
B = Existing plasma devices.
C = Gaseous discharges.
D = Astrophysical and geophysical plasmas.
E = High vacuum devices in a strong magnetic field (cyclotrons, gauges, magnetrons, etc.).

5.5 Numerical Values for Five Typical Cases

Table 5.2 contains the numerical values of A and of various other parameters for five typical plasmas represented by the points P_1, P_2, P_3, P_4, and P_5 of Fig. 5.1. The computations have been made with $m = 1836$ (electron-proton plasma).

CHAPTER 6

The Four Modes of Propagation in the General Case ($B_T \neq 0$)

In the preceding chapters we have seen that, in the absence of a transverse magnetic field, there exist two purely transverse and two purely longitudinal waves. The existence of a transverse field B_T seriously complicates the situation. The field introduces a coupling between transverse and longitudinal motion of the particles. There thus appear mixed modes having, simultaneously, transverse and longitudinal components. In this chapter we shall attempt to extricate the rules governing these mixed modes. In this discussion, we assume the collision frequencies are zero. The calculations will thus be simplified and can be carried much further.

6.1 General Dispersion Relation

a. Existence and orthogonality of four modes. The general dispersion relation in Table 2.2 can be considered as an equation for the determination of y, the index of refraction of the waves, as a function of x, the frequency. It is of fourth degree in y. In Appendix 2 we show, still limiting ourselves to the case where the collisions are negligible, that this equation always has four real roots. Since y is equal to the square of the index, the index itself is either real or purely imaginary; there always exist four modes of propagation corresponding to waves which are either unattenuated or else strictly evanescent. This conclusion is physically rather evident since it depends on the absence of any energy dissipation effect. Had we included collisions, we would have found that the roots of the equation for y are complex.

The proof that the four roots are real is nevertheless instructive, and here it is, in principle. Note that Table 2.2 is symmetrized when $\nu = \nu_{en} = \nu_{in} = 0$, and also that the equation for y written in the determinantal form is a great deal like the eigenvalue equation of a matrix. However, only four diagonal terms contain the unknown y. This suggests an attempt, after eliminating five of the variables, to construct from the dispersion equation an analogous eigenvalue equation for a symmetric matrix of fourth order. This computation is developed in Appendix 2 and shows that we can carry out this transformation by eliminating the variables v_{ex}, v_{ix}, v_{ey}, v_{iy}, and E_z. Consequently, from an established theorem, the four eigenvalues of the symmetric matrix, which are the four roots of y of the dispersion equation, are real [see Ref. 16, p. 174.]

The four variables

$$z_1 = E_x, \; z_2 = jE_y, \; z_3 = v_{ez} \frac{m_e \omega_p}{q_e \sqrt{\epsilon_e}}, \; z_4 = v_{iz} \frac{m_i \Omega_p}{q_i \sqrt{\epsilon_i}} \quad (1)$$

which are not eliminated, theoretically constitute a natural group of variables for the study of wave propagation. We note in particular that the z_n are the variables which express the average energy flux N_z and N'_z, Eq. (5.26).

We also know that the four eigenvectors of a symmetric matrix are orthogonal. Let u_1, u_2, u_3, u_4 be these four eigenvectors (vectors in z_1, z_2, z_3, z_4 space) which represent the four modes of propagation. If, at a point in the plasma, we consider a plane wave u of frequency ω but of arbitrary polarization (that is, corresponding to any value of the four coordinates z), we can always represent this perturbation as the superposition of the four modes of propagation. We then write

$$u = \alpha_1 u_1 + \alpha_2 u_2 + \alpha_3 u_3 + \alpha_4 u_4 \quad (2)$$

The α's are the relative complex amplitudes of each mode. Since the speed of propagation of the four modes is, in general, different, the wave (2) distorts as it propagates.

In addition, if we consider any two modes u_a and u_b of components z_a and z_b, there exists between these components the orthogonality condition

$$\sum_{n=1}^{4} z_{na} z_{nb}^* = 0 \qquad (a \neq b) \tag{3}$$

which can also be written in the form

$$\frac{E_{xa}E_{xb}^* + jE_{ya}(jE_{yb})^*}{8\pi} + \tfrac{1}{2} n_e m_e V_e^2 v_{eza} \, v_{ezb}^* \tag{4}$$

$$+ \tfrac{1}{2} n_i m_i V_i^2 v_{iza} \, v_{izb}^* = 0$$

We can verify that this relation is satisfied for the case $B_T = 0$, studied in Chapters 3 and 4. This result is obvious when one of the modes considered is transverse and the other longitudinal. The result also emerges when the two modes are transverse. According to Eqs. (3.12), we have

$$E_{ya}/E_{xa} = + j \qquad \text{for the ordinary wave}$$

$$E_{yb}/E_{xb} = - j \qquad \text{for the extraordinary wave}$$

For the two cases of ion and electron longitudinal modes, the orthogonality condition, Eq. (4), leads to the equation

$$(v_{eza}/v_{iza}) \, (v_{ezb}/v_{izb}) = - \, n_i m_i V_i^2/n_e m_e V_e^2 = - \, \tau \tag{5}$$

This equation can be verified from the discussion in Chapter 4.

b. Wave polarization. If we refer to Table A2.1 we see that the nine variables which correspond to a real matrix (with $\nu = \nu_{en} = \nu_{in} = 0$) are*

$$E_x, \frac{v_{ex}}{j} \frac{m_e \omega_p}{q_e}, \frac{v_{ix}}{j} \frac{m_i \Omega_p}{q_i}, jE_y, v_{ey} \frac{m_e \omega_p}{q_e},$$

$$v_{iy} \frac{m_i \Omega_p}{q_i}, jE_z, v_{ez} \frac{m_e \omega_p}{q_e \, (\epsilon_e)^{1/2}}, v_{iz} \frac{m_i \Omega_p}{q_i \, (\epsilon_i)^{1/2}}$$

For a given wave solution of the dispersion equation, the values

---

*These variables are slightly different from those in Table 2.2 due to the transformations carried out in Appendix 2.

of these four components are given by the rule of minors to within a constant factor. Since all the terms of the matrix in Table A2.1 are real, we can conclude some general properties concerning the polarization of the waves:

1. The electron and ion velocity components along a given axis are in phase (or in opposite phase). This phase is also that of the corresponding component of the electric current according to Eq. (1.13).

2. The components of the electric field and of the velocity of the particles on the same axis are in quadrature. Hence the electric field also varies in quadrature with the current. This result is evident from Eqs. (2.15), (2.16), and (2.17) when k^2c^2/ω^2 is real.

3. The ratio of the current component J_z to J_y is real, and the ratio of these two components to J_x is imaginary. Hence the current vector **J** describes an ellipse whose plane is perpendicular to the yz plane. One axis is situated along the x axis and the other in the yz plane.

4. Similarly, the ratio of the components E_z and E_y is real, and the ratio of these two components to E_x is imaginary. Hence the vector **E** describes an ellipse whose plane is perpendicular to the yz plane and whose axes are situated along the x axis and in the yz plane.

5. Finally, from Eqs. (2.15) and (2.16) we conclude

$$E_x/E_y = J_x/J_y$$

The projection of the two ellipses described by **E** and **J** on the xy plane are similar.

We can now represent the structure of the waves in the general case by Fig. 6.1. According to these general properties, it is sufficient in order to characterize the "polarization of the wave" to specify the value of the three ratios of those fundamental variables E_x, E_y, v_{ez}, and v_{iz} from which we can obtain all the others. It is generally useful to choose the ratios E_y/jE_x, transverse polarization; v_{ez}/v_{iz}, ratio of electron to ion velocities; and E_z/E_y, angle of the electric oscillation with respect to the plane of the wave, since E_z is determined from v_{ez} and v_{iz} with Eq. (2.17).

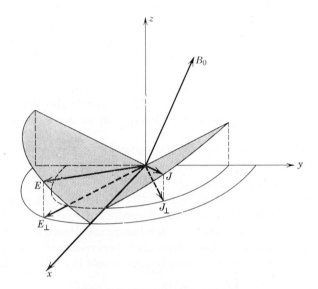

Fig. 6.1. General wave structure.

These general properties of the polarization of waves are clearly satisfied in the two specific cases studied in Chapters 3 and 4. For the transverse waves ($v_{ez} = v_{iz} = 0$) we have found from Eq. (3.12) that the ratio E_y/E_x is equal to $-j$ for the extraordinary wave y_{II} and to $+j$ for the ordinary wave y_{I}. For the longitudinal waves ($E_x = E_y = 0$) the ratio v_{ez}/v_{iz} is real and positive for the ion wave and real and negative for the electron wave. For each of these waves the sign of this ratio remains the same over the entire frequency domain and therefore represents a characteristic property. One must underscore that this is, in general, no longer the case for the four modes which we study in this chapter ($B_{\text{T}} \neq 0$). The equations useful for the general study of polarization are given in Appendix 4.

c. Expansion of the determinant (Eq. 2.2). The expansion of the determinant, Eq. (2.2), can be effected in successive powers of ω_T and Ω_T by using well-known rules. Thus we can write a dispersion relation in the form

$$\Delta_T \Delta_L + B + C + D + E = 0 \tag{6}$$

$$\Delta_T = \Delta_1{}^2 + \frac{\omega_L{}^2 \Omega_L{}^2}{\omega^4} (y - 1)^2 - \frac{\omega_L{}^2}{\omega^2} \left(y - 1 + \frac{\Omega_p{}^2}{\omega^2} \right)^2$$
$$- \frac{\Omega_L{}^2}{\omega^2} \left(y - 1 + \frac{\omega_p{}^2}{\omega^2} \right)^2 + 2 \frac{\omega_L \Omega_L \omega_p{}^2 \Omega_p{}^2}{\omega^6} \tag{7}$$

$$\Delta_L = \left(1 - \frac{y}{\epsilon_e} \right) \left(1 - \frac{y}{\epsilon_i} \right) - x \left(1 - \frac{y}{\epsilon_s} \right) \tag{8}$$

$$B = \frac{\omega_T{}^2}{\omega^2} \left(\frac{y}{\epsilon_i} - 1 + \frac{\Omega_p{}^2}{\omega^2} \right) \left[\Delta_1 \left(y - 1 + \frac{\Omega_p{}^2}{\omega^2} \right) \right.$$
$$\left. - \frac{\Omega_L{}^2}{\omega^2} (y - 1) \left(y - 1 + \frac{\omega_p{}^2}{\omega^2} \right) \right] \tag{9}$$

$$C = \frac{\Omega_T{}^2}{\omega^2} \left(\frac{y}{\epsilon_e} - 1 + \frac{\omega_p{}^2}{\omega^2} \right) \left[\Delta_1 \left(y - 1 + \frac{\omega_p{}^2}{\omega^2} \right) \right.$$
$$\left. - \frac{\omega_L{}^2}{\omega^2} (y - 1) \left(y - 1 + \frac{\Omega_p{}^2}{\omega^2} \right) \right] \tag{10}$$

$$D = 2 \frac{\omega_T \Omega_T \omega_p{}^2 \Omega_p{}^2}{\omega^6} \left[- \Delta_1 + (y - 1) \frac{\omega_L \Omega_L}{\omega^2} \right] \tag{11}$$

$$E = \frac{\omega_T{}^2 \Omega_T{}^2}{\omega^4} (y - 1) \Delta_1 \tag{12}$$

$$\Delta_1 = y - 1 + x \tag{13}$$

Δ_T is the determinant of the two transverse waves. In the absence of a magnetic field, it specializes to $\Delta_1{}^2$. Δ_L is the determinant of the two longitudinal waves. Equation (6) is completely symmetric with respect to electrons and ions. It is of sixth degree in x and y, of fourth degree in y alone, and of third degree in x alone.

6.2   Properties of the Dispersion Curve

a. General picture and special cases. The complete discussion of Eq. (6) is summarized in Appendix 3. We show, in this chapter, the results of these detailed computations.

In general, if Eq. (6) is considered as a function of x, we obtain an equation of third degree in x. Since the dispersion curve is of sixth degree, this result proves that it has three horizontal asymptotes. Similarly, if the equation is arranged as a function of the variable y, we obtain an equation of the fourth degree in y. This result shows that the curve possesses, in addition, two vertical asymptotes. The sixth asymptote is oblique.

However, detailed computations show two special cases for which the order of the equations is lowered; some branches of the curve and their asymptotes are moved to infinity. These two special cases will be treated subsequently. They are (1) transverse propagation ($B_L = 0$) (see Chapter 7), and (2) the case of cold plasmas ($V_e = V_i = 0$) (see Chapter 8).

b. High frequency waves; nomenclature for the four modes. When x goes to zero, that is, when the frequency goes to

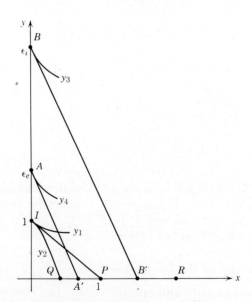

Fig. 6.2. Mode properties in the high frequency region: y_1, ordinary mode; y_2, extraordinary mode; y_3, ion mode; y_4, electron mode.

infinity, the dispersion curve has the form shown in Fig. 6.2. It goes through the three fixed points I (twice), A, and B. The ordinates of the points I, A, and B are, respectively, 1, ϵ_e, and ϵ_i. They are independent of the magnetic field; this property allows us to identify four modes of propagation. If we designate by y_1, y_2, y_3, y_4 the four roots in Fig. 6.2, they can be labeled as follows: (1) y_1, ordinary mode; (2) y_2, extraordinary mode; (3) y_3, ion mode; and (4) y_4, electron mode.

For small values of x, these four solutions can be expressed by the following expansions:

$$y_1 = 1 - x + \left(\frac{\omega_L - \Omega_L}{\omega_0}\right) x^{3/2} + \cdots \tag{14}$$

$$y_2 = 1 - x - \left(\frac{\omega_L - \Omega_L}{\omega_0}\right) x^{3/2} + \cdots \tag{15}$$

$$y_3 = \epsilon_i \left[1 + \left(\frac{1 - 1/\epsilon_s}{\epsilon_i/\epsilon_e - 1} - \frac{\Omega_T^2}{\omega_0^2}\right) x + \cdots \right]$$
$$\simeq \epsilon_i \left[1 - \frac{\Omega_p^2 + \Omega_T^2}{\omega^2} x + \cdots \right] \tag{16}$$

$$y_4 = \epsilon_e \left[1 + \left(\frac{1 - 1/\epsilon_s}{\epsilon_e/\epsilon_i - 1} - \frac{\omega_T^2}{\omega_0^2}\right) x + \cdots \right]$$
$$\simeq \epsilon_e \left[1 - \frac{\omega_p^2 + \omega_T^2}{\omega^2} + \cdots \right] \tag{17}$$

The second expressions given for y_3 and y_4 are valid approximations for $\epsilon_s \gg 1$, $m \gg 1$, and $\tau = 1$.

The two curves for the ordinary and the extraordinary modes have the same tangent at point I. This tangent goes through the point P $(x = 1)$ on the x axis. The curvatures of the two modes at I are of opposite sign. The tangents at A and B of the curves representing the electron and ion modes, in general, intersect the x axis at the following points respectively:

$$\text{A}': x = \omega_0^2/(\omega_p^2 + \omega_T^2) \qquad \text{and} \qquad \text{B}': x = \omega_0^2/(\Omega_p^2 - \Omega_T^2)$$

c. Resonance frequencies. By the term resonance frequencies, we mean those values of ω which make the index of refraction infinite; these frequencies correspond to the vertical asymptotes of the dispersion curve. Equation (A3.10) shows that the resonance frequencies are

$$\omega = \omega_L \tag{18}$$

$$\omega = \Omega_L \tag{19}$$

with the condition, however, that $B_L \neq 0$, $V_e \neq 0$, $V_i \neq 0$ (see Chapters 7 and 8)

d. Critical frequencies. By the term critical frequencies, we mean the values of ω for which the index of refraction is zero. When a branch of the dispersion curve goes through a critical point, this constitutes a transition between the regime where the waves propagate without attenuation and the regime where the waves are purely evanescent. There exist three critical frequencies given by the formulas

$$\omega = \omega_0 \tag{20}$$

$$\omega = \omega_1 = \tfrac{1}{2}\{[(\omega_b + \Omega_b)^2 + 4\omega_0{}^2]^{1/2} - (\omega_b - \Omega_b)\} \tag{21}$$

$$\omega = \omega_2 = \tfrac{1}{2}\{[(\omega_b + \Omega_b)^2 + 4\omega_0{}^2]^{1/2} + (\omega_b - \Omega_b)\} \tag{22}$$

These three frequencies are independent of V_e and V_i. They are the three points where the dispersion curve intersects the x axis, and we shall label them, respectively, P, R, and Q. The position of point P ($x = 1$) is independent of the plasma density and of the value of the magnetic field. The positions of the two other critical points, R and Q, are independent of the orientation of the magnetic field but depend on its magnitude. The point Q is always to the left of both P and the first vertical asymptote, since

$$\omega_2 > \omega_0 \tag{23}$$

$$\omega_2 > \omega_b \geqslant \omega_L$$

The relative positions of P and R depend on the plasma density. We have:

$\omega_1 > \omega_0$ (R to the left of P) for $A < 1/m$ (very rarified plasmas).
$\omega_1 < \omega_0$ (R to the right of P) for $A > 1/m$ (rarified, moderately dense or dense plasmas).

When the plasma density goes to zero, the two critical frequencies ω_1 and ω_2, respectively, go to Ω_b and ω_b; when the density goes to infinity, ω_1 and ω_2 go to ω_0.

e. Limits of the speed of low frequency waves; magneto-dynamic waves (horizontal asymptotes of the dispersion curve). In general, the dispersion curve has three horizontal asymptotes. Physically, these asymptotes represent the low frequency waves. These magnetodynamic waves are similar to the hydrodynamic waves which can propagate in a nonionized fluid.

In Appendix 3 the computation of the position of the horizontal asymptotes is carried out; it leads to the following three solutions:

$$y_2 = \epsilon_a(1 + s) \qquad (24)$$

$$y_{1,3} = \frac{(\epsilon_a + \epsilon_s - 1)\,(1 + s) + 1}{2} +$$
$$\frac{\epsilon\sqrt{[(\epsilon_a + \epsilon_s - 1)\,(1 + s) - 1]^2 - 4(\epsilon_a - 1)\,(\epsilon_s - 1)\,(1 + s)}}{2} \qquad (25)$$

$$s = \tan^2 \theta \qquad (26)$$

where θ is the angle between the direction of propagation z and the magnetic field and $\epsilon = +1$ for y_1 and to -1 for y_3.

Equations (24) and (25) are useful for the study of the change in position of the asymptotes as a function of θ when all the other parameters (density and plasma temperature, magnetic field) are assumed fixed. In all cases, we show that

$$y_1 \geqslant y_2 \geqslant y_3 \qquad (27)$$

The detailed discussion of the properties of magnetodynamic waves is carried out in Chapter 9.

f. Oblique asymptotes. The dispersion curve has three horizontal and two vertical asymptotes; as it is of sixth order, there is usually another asymptote, necessarily oblique. The equation for this asymptote (Appendix 3, Section A3.6) is

$$y = - (\epsilon_e \epsilon_i / \epsilon_s)\, x + 1 + (\epsilon_e + \epsilon_i - \epsilon_s - 1)\, (1 + \tan^2 \theta) \quad (28)$$

This asymptote has a negative slope that is independent of the magnetic field. We are already cognizant of its existence from the study of longitudinal propagation. In that case, this asymptote corresponds to the evanescent branch of plasma oscillations. The position of the asymptote depends on the orientation of the magnetic field but not on its magnitude. In the limit of transverse propagation, it disappears to infinity. This case will be studied in Chapter 7. Equation (28) is greatly simplified in almost all the usual cases since, in general,

$$V_i^2 \ll V_e^2 \ll c^2$$

$$\Omega_p^2 \ll \omega_p^2$$

$$V_s^2 = 2V_i^2$$

Equation (28) then becomes

$$y = - 2\epsilon_e x + (\epsilon_i / 2)\, (1 + \tan^2 \theta) \quad (29)$$

6.3   Double Points of the Dispersion Curve; General Definition of the Four Modes

In the preceding paragraphs we have seen that the dispersion curve always has two double points (I and the point infinity on the y axis) and a triple point (infinity on the x axis). It is very important to know if there also exist other double points at finite values. At a double point, two different modes have the same phase velocity, and we should expect that this introduces nonlinear effects, causing coupling between the modes. We have eliminated nonlinear effects in our theory. Therefore, double points can be called coupling points.

These double points raise a problem in the continuation of the modes. Where there exists a double point M, the following convention is adopted: we attribute the four segments of the curves to the two modes in such a way that the resultant modes *do not fully intersect*. This is illustrated for the hypothetical modes i and j in Fig. 6.3. This convention allows us to link, unequivocally, the high frequency to the low frequency regimes while taking into account the various asymptotes which we have studied. The resultant pattern is shown in Fig. 6.4. The notations previously

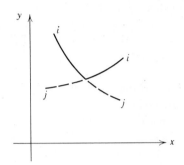

Fig. 6.3.

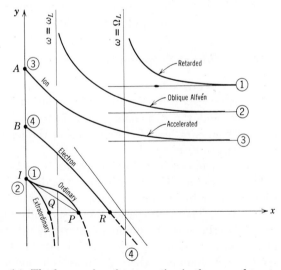

Fig. 6.4. The four modes of propagation in the general treatment.

introduced in the two regimes of high and low frequencies have actually been chosen in a coherent manner: they are recalled by the indices 1, 2, 3, 4 indicated in the various curves of Fig. 6.4. The labels used for the three low frequency waves will be justified in Chapter 9.

In Fig. 6.4 we see that the magnetodynamic wave whose velocity is smallest, the retarded wave, corresponds to the ordinary mode y_1 and that the accelerated magnetodynamic wave, whose velocity is largest, corresponds to the ion mode y_3. Finally, the wave of intermediate velocity, or Alfvén wave, corresponds to the extraordinary mode y_2.

The double points are not easy to study in detail because of our burdensome dispersion relation. We shall, however, eventually consider two individual cases: the propagation of transverse and of longitudinal waves. In these two cases, while the dispersion curve is of the sixth degree, it degenerates into two curves of lower degree. The points of intersection of these two curves are coupling points. In the general case (B_T, $B_L \neq 0$) it seems that there would be no more additional coupling points in the finite plane. We are not, however, aware of any proof of this property.

6.4 Quasi-longitudinal Propagation

a. Behavior of the curve in the neighborhood of a coupling point. If B_T is rigorously zero, the dispersion relation is reduced to $\Delta_T \cdot \Delta_L = 0$, and the dispersion curve is made up of the superposition of curves C_T and C_L, representing the longitudinal and transverse waves, respectively.

For $B_T \ll B_L$, we can consider the terms other than $\Delta_T \Delta_L$ in Eq. (6) as small perturbations. The result is that the dispersion curve separates itself rather little from the dispersion curve for longitudinal propagation. The perturbations are especially important only in the neighborhood of the points of intersection between C_T and C_L. This is the case along a portion of C situated in the neighborhood of C_L, for example, where Δ_T takes on non-negligible values. Thus according to Eq. (6) we have

$$\Delta_L = O(B_T^2)/\Delta_T$$

The separation of C from C_L is of second order in B_T. C also contains arcs which follow the curve C_T to second order.

When, by following one of these arcs, we approach one of the points of intersection of C_T and C_L, Δ_T and Δ_L become, a priori, of the same order, and the curve C ought to separate from the intersection of C_T and C_L by an amount which is now only of the

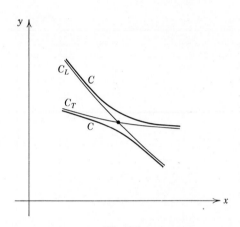

Fig. 6.5.

first order with respect to B_T. The points of intersection of C_T and C_L are points where the longitudinal and transverse wave are coupled to each other. In the neighborhood of one of these points, the dispersion curve for a quasi-longitudinal propagation has the appearance shown in Fig. 6.5. The linking is done without the tangent ever becoming vertical (otherwise, in the neighborhood of the coupling point, the dispersion equation would have two imaginary roots, and we have shown that the roots are always real).

b. General behavior of curves C_T and C_L. Points of coupling. The general behavior and the relative position of the curves C_T and C_L depend essentially on the positions of the asymptotes. Let us recall that we have

$\epsilon_a \simeq 1$, in rarified and very rarified plasmas

$\epsilon_a \gg 1$, in moderately dense and dense plasmas

$\epsilon_a < \epsilon_s$, in plasmas of all types except the very dense, unconfined plasmas.

The curves C_T and C_L have, in general, eight meeting points real or imaginary. The point at infinity on the x axis counts for two. Thus there remain six meeting points in the finite region. We are

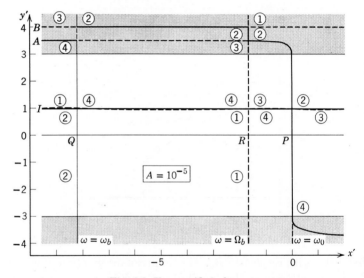

Fig. 6.6. Very rarified plasmas.

only interested in those which are real. A simple qualitative study of the position of various elements of C_L and C_T show that the six coupling points are real if the plasma density is very small. The position of the curve is then that of Fig. 6.6. It is difficult to pinpoint the conditions for which the points of coupling are real. These conditions depend, in general, on the density and the temperature of the plasma. We realize, however, that, regardless of the temperature, the relative position of the curves changes rapidly when the density goes through the two values which give $\omega_0 = \Omega_b$ and $\omega_0 = \omega_b$.

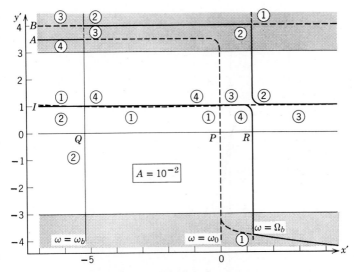

Fig. 6.7. Rarified plasmas.

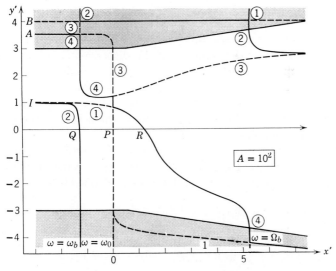

Fig. 6.8. Moderately dense plasmas.

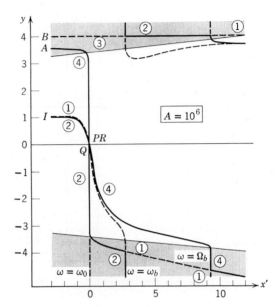

Fig. 6.9. Dense plasmas (confined).

c. Dispersion curves for five typical plasmas. Figures 6.6 through 6.10 show the behavior of the dispersion curve for longitudinal propagation for the five typical plasmas defined in Chapter 5. The drawings are for the case $Z = 1$, $m_i = 1836\, m_e$. The dispersion curves for quasi-longitudinal propagation can be obtained from them by rounding out the corners in the neighborhood of the three coupling points.

In order to show graphically the numerical results, we had to adopt, unfortunately, scales which greatly contract the coordinates. We have made use of the variables x' and y' defined by

$$y' = 1 + \log\,(1 + \log y) \qquad \text{for } y \geqslant 1$$

$$y' = y \qquad \text{for } -1 \leqslant y \leqslant 1 \tag{30}$$

$$y' = -\,[1 + \log\,(1 + \log |y|)] \qquad \text{for } y \leqslant -1$$

$$x' = \log x \tag{31}$$

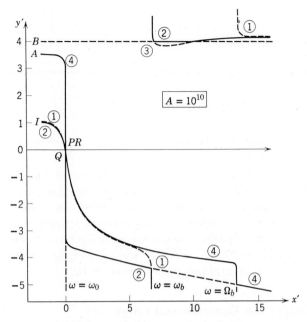

Fig. 6.10. Dense plasmas (unconfined).

Figure 7.2 contains a comparison scale of the values of y and y'.

To bring out the manner in which the four modes degenerate to give, in the case of longitudinal propagation, the two longitudinal and the two transverse waves, we have adopted in Figs. 6.6 to 6.9 the following graphical convention:

1. Arcs which correspond to the modes y_1 and y_3 are represented by a dashed line.

2. Arcs which correspond to the modes y_2 and y_4 are represented by a continuous line.

In addition, we have noted next to each arc the number of the corresponding mode. We can verify from these curves what we have indicated in Chapter 5, Section 5.4: for $A < 1$ (Figs. 6.6 and 6.7) the indices of refraction for the transverse waves are always very nearly unity except in the neighborhood of resonances.

CHAPTER 7

Transverse Propagation ($B_L = 0$)

Propagation in a direction perpendicular to the magnetic field constitutes a limiting case of general propagation [17]. In this chapter we study this case showing the manner in which the four fundamental modes degenerate. We derive a singular wave with linear polarization parallel to the magnetic field which propagates as if this field were zero, and other waves which have an elliptical polarization in the xz plane, perpendicular to B_0.

7.1 Dispersion Equation and Curve

When ω_L and Ω_L are zero, we can factor out the determinant Δ_1 in the dispersion equation. This factor corresponds to a wave which propagates as if there were no magnetic field. Neglecting this singular wave for the moment, we can simplify the dispersion equation, Eq. (6.6).

$$
\begin{aligned}
(y - 1 + x) &\left[\left(1 - \frac{y}{\epsilon_e}\right)\left(1 - \frac{y}{\epsilon_i}\right) - x\left(1 - \frac{y}{\epsilon_s}\right) \right] \\
&+ \frac{\omega_T^2}{\omega^2}\left(\frac{y}{\epsilon_i} - 1 + \frac{\Omega_p^2}{\omega^2}\right)\left(y - 1 + \frac{\Omega_p^2}{\omega^2}\right) \\
&+ \frac{\Omega_T^2}{\omega^2}\left(\frac{y}{\epsilon_e} - 1 + \frac{\omega_p^2}{\omega^2}\right)\left(y - 1 + \frac{\omega_p^2}{\omega^2}\right) \\
&- 2\frac{\omega_T\Omega_T\omega_p^2\Omega_p^2}{\omega^6} + (y - 1)\frac{\omega_T^2\Omega_T^2}{\omega^4} = 0
\end{aligned}
\tag{1}
$$

Introducing the parameters A and m, expanding, and grouping in powers of x, we obtain

$$
\left[\left(1 + \frac{1}{A}\right)\left(\frac{y}{\epsilon_s} - 1 + \frac{1}{A}(y-1)\right)\right]x^2
$$
$$
- \left\{\frac{1}{A}(y-1)\left[m\left(1 - \frac{y}{\epsilon_i}\right) + \frac{1}{m}\left(1 - \frac{y}{\epsilon_e}\right)\right]\right.
$$
$$
\left. + (y-1)\left(1 - \frac{y}{\epsilon_s}\right) - \left(1 - \frac{y}{\epsilon_e}\right)\left(1 - \frac{y}{\epsilon_i}\right)\right\}x
$$
$$
+ (y-1)\left(1 - \frac{y}{\epsilon_e}\right)\left(1 - \frac{y}{\epsilon_i}\right) = 0 \tag{2}
$$

This equation is of third order in x and y. Hence, the dispersion curve contains the line IP ($\Delta_1 = 0$) and the cubic equation represented by Eq. (2). We consider first the properties of the latter.

1. The only term in y^3 in Eq. (2) is $y^3/\epsilon_e\epsilon_i$. This term cannot be null except in the particular case of cold plasmas (see Chapter 8). Hence, the dispersion curve has no vertical asymptote. This result is not surprising; the two resonances $\omega = \omega_L$ and $\omega = \Omega_L$ obtained in the general case are here pushed out toward the right of the figures to infinity.

2. There is a horizontal asymptote which is obtained by setting the coefficient of $x^2 = 0$.

$$
y = (1 + A)\epsilon_s/(A + \epsilon_s) = \epsilon_a\epsilon_s/(\epsilon_a + \epsilon_s - 1) \tag{3}
$$

Therefore, there exists only one magnetodynamic wave. Referring to Fig. 6.4, we see that it is the accelerated wave, the two upper arcs having been pushed out to infinity.

3. Finally, there are two oblique asymptotes. We can write their equations in the parametric form

$$
y = ax + b \tag{4}
$$

To find a and b, we substitute this form into Eq. (2). By successively setting to zero the third degree terms in the product of x and y and then the second degree terms, we determine the coefficients a

and b for these two asymptotes by means of the equations

$$\frac{a^2}{\epsilon_e \epsilon_i} + \left[\frac{1}{\epsilon_s} + \frac{1}{\epsilon_e \epsilon_i} + \frac{1}{A}\left(\frac{m}{\epsilon_i} + \frac{1}{m\epsilon_e}\right)\right] a$$

$$+ \left(1 + \frac{1}{A}\right)\left(\frac{1}{\epsilon_s} + \frac{1}{A}\right) = 0 \tag{5}$$

$$b\left[\frac{a^2}{\epsilon_e \epsilon_i} - \left(1 + \frac{1}{A}\right)\left(\frac{1}{\epsilon_s} + \frac{1}{A}\right)\right] = a^2\left(\frac{1}{\epsilon_e} + \frac{1}{\epsilon_i}\right)$$

$$+ a\left[1 + \frac{1}{\epsilon_e} + \frac{1}{\epsilon_i} - \frac{1}{\epsilon_e \epsilon_i} + \frac{1}{A}\left(m + \frac{1}{m}\right)\right] \tag{6}$$

$$+ \left(1 + \frac{1}{A}\right)\left(1 - \frac{1}{\epsilon_s}\right)$$

The general discussion of Eqs. (5) and (6) is complicated [18]. We can, however, show that Eq. (5) always has two real negative roots whose absolute values are greater than unity.

Using the general definitions given in Section 6.3, the position of the three asymptotes enables us to associate the various portions of the cubic equation and the line $\Delta_1 = 0$ with the four fundamental modes. This is shown schematically in Fig. 7.1.

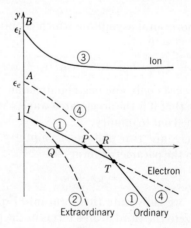

Fig. 7.1.

There exists a coupling point T at the intersection of the cubic and the line IP. The singular wave is associated with the ordinary mode to the left of T and with the electron mode to the right of T. The ordinate of T is

$$y = \frac{2 + 1/A - (m + 1/m)}{1 + \dfrac{1}{\epsilon_s} + \dfrac{1}{A} - \dfrac{m}{\epsilon_i} - \dfrac{1}{m\epsilon_e}} \simeq \frac{1/A - m}{1 + 1/A} \qquad (7)$$

The sign of this ordinate shows that the coupling point T occurs for evanescent waves in all plasmas except those called very rarified.

Exact dispersion curves as a function of x' and y' (see Eqs. 6.30 and 6.31) are shown in Fig. 7.2 for the representative plasma P_3. To illustrate the manner in which the modes are transformed, we have drawn on this figure those dispersion curves which show the longitudinal propagation using continuous lines and those which

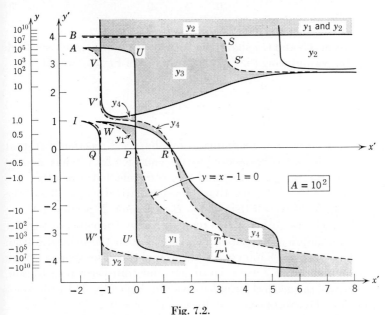

Fig. 7.2.

show the transverse propagation in dashes. The shadowed areas are the regions occupied by the various modes in the intermediate case of oblique propagation. Figure 7.2 shows that there are sections of the curve which are almost vertical (arcs SS', TT', UU', VV', WW'). Along these arcs the index varies very rapidly as a function of frequency. We call these pseudo-resonances. We shall again find these pseudo-resonances in the cold plasma treatment of Chapter 8; there they are called resonances.

7.2 Wave Polarization

By referring to Table 2.2 we see that the dispersion equation for transverse propagation can be written symbolically by representing each of the nine 3×3 determinants which form it by a single letter.

$$\begin{vmatrix} \Delta_1 & 0 & C_T \\ 0 & \Delta_1 & 0 \\ C'_T & 0 & \Delta_T \end{vmatrix} = 0 \tag{8}$$

The terms C_T and C'_T show the coupling due to the transverse field, B_T. By permutating the lines and columns of Eq. (8), we get

$$\begin{vmatrix} \Delta_1 & 0 & 0 \\ \hline 0 & \Delta_1 & C_T \\ 0 & C'_T & \Delta_T \end{vmatrix} = \Delta_1 \begin{vmatrix} \Delta_1 & C_T \\ C'_T & \Delta_1 \end{vmatrix} = 0 \tag{9}$$

In this form we see, reasoning as in Chapter 2 (Section 2.3), that the singular wave represented by the equation $\Delta_1 = 0$ has nonzero components E_y, v_{ey}, and v_{iy} and zero components in the other two directions. This wave has thus a linear polarization parallel to the magnetic field (recall that $B_T = B_y$; Chapter 2, Section 2.1).

Similarly, the other waves represented by the cubic of Fig. 7.1 have an elliptic polarization perpendicular to the magnetic field. We have seen in Chapter 6 that the axes of this ellipse coincide with the spatial x and z axes. To understand transverse polarization, we invoke the general formulas given in Appendix 4. In the present case, these formulas yield, for $1 - x - y \neq 0$:

$$E_x = a\left[\left(1 - p^2 - t^2 - \frac{y}{\epsilon_e}\right)\left(1 - P^2 - T^2 - \frac{y}{\epsilon_i}\right) - p^2P^2\right] \quad (10)$$

$$v_{ez}\frac{m_e\omega_p}{q_e} = a\left[\left(1 - P^2 - T^2 - \frac{y}{\epsilon_i}\right)pt - pPPT\right] \quad (11)$$

$$v_{iz}\frac{m_i\Omega_p}{q_i} = -a\left[\left(1 - p^2 - t^2 - \frac{y}{\epsilon_e}\right)PT - pPpt\right] \quad (12)$$

$$E_z = ja\left[p^2t\left(1 - \frac{y}{\epsilon_i}\right) - P^2T\left(1 - \frac{y}{\epsilon_e}\right)\right] \quad (13)$$

These equations show that E_x/jE_z is negative for modes 2 and 3 of Fig. 7.1 and positive for the remaining branch of the curve which passes through the point T. The ellipse of polarization is thus described from the x axis to the z axis for branches 2 and 3 and in the opposite direction for the branch which goes through the point T.

CHAPTER 8

Propagation in Cold Plasmas

In this chapter we consider the propagation of waves while ignoring the thermal motion of particles. This approximation, which consists of setting $V_e = V_i = 0$, is known as the cold plasma approximation [19]. This condition is clearly satisfied by a plasma at zero temperature. However, we shall see that it is also applicable to plasmas at rather high temperatures. Intuitively, we conclude that this approximation is valid whenever the phase velocity of the wave is much larger than V_e and V_i; we are then not in the neighborhood of A or B, near a resonance, nor on the dispersion curve for the retarded magnetodynamic mode (see Fig. 6.4).

We have indicated that, from the standpoint of the general theory of propagation, the case of cold plasmas is a singular case. We shall, however, see that this singularity is much different from those we have encountered in longitudinal or in transverse propagation; a coupling point does not appear. The four modes keep their identity; however, each mode exists only in a specified frequency band. At each frequency two of the modes are pushed out to infinity by the condition $V_e = V_i = 0$, so that it would appear as if there were only two modes rather than all four.

The cold plasma approximation has been primarily studied in the high frequency region, where we can make the additional assumption that ion displacement is negligible. This approximation, due to Appleton and Hartree, is obtained by setting $1/m_i = \Omega_b = \Omega_p = 0$. At the end of this chapter the essential formulas of this approximation are related to the general formulas. For additional details the reader is referred to books which treat this question more specifically, especially to the recent work of J. A. Ratcliffe [20].

3.1 Dispersion Equation and Curve

It is now convenient to write the dispersion relation with respect to the variable $u = y - 1$. Substituting in Eqs. (A3.10) through (A3.14)

$$1/\epsilon_e = 1/\epsilon_i = 1/\epsilon_s = 0$$

we obtain

$$
\begin{aligned}
&\left[(1 - x) \left(1 - \frac{\omega_L^2}{\omega^2} \right) \left(1 - \frac{\Omega_L^2}{\omega^2} \right) + x \left(1 - \frac{\omega_L \Omega_L}{\omega^2} \right) \frac{\omega_T^2 \Omega_T^2}{\omega^2} \right. \\
&\left. \quad - \frac{\omega_T^2 + \Omega_T^2}{\omega^2} + \frac{\omega_L \Omega_L \Omega_T \omega_T}{\omega^4} + \frac{\omega_T^2 \Omega_T^2}{\omega^4} \right] u^2 \\
&+ \left[2x (1 - x) \left(1 - \frac{\omega_L \Omega_L}{\omega^2} \right) + x^2 \frac{\omega_T \Omega_T}{\omega^2} \right. \\
&\left. \quad - x \left(1 - \frac{\omega_L \Omega_L}{\omega^2} \right) \frac{\omega_T \Omega_T}{\omega^2} - x \frac{\omega_T^2 + \Omega_T^2}{\omega^2} + x \frac{\omega_T^2 \Omega_T^2}{\omega^4} \right] u \\
&\qquad\qquad + x^2 \left(1 - x - \frac{\omega_T \Omega_T}{\omega^2} \right) = 0
\end{aligned}
\tag{1}
$$

This equation is of fifth degree with respect to u and x, of second degree with respect to u alone, and of third degree with respect to x alone. The dispersion curve is of fifth degree and possesses three vertical and two horizontal asymptotes. Hence, there exists three resonances and two magnetodynamic waves. This stems from the fact that V_s is zero; the arc of the curve representing the retarded wave in Fig. 6.4 is then pushed upward to infinity.

3.2 Vertical Asymptotes: Resonance Frequencies

a. General equation. The vertical asymptotes are obtained by nulling the coefficient of u^2 in Eq. (1). Setting, as before, $s = \tan^2\theta$

and introducing A and m, we obtain the following third degree equation in x:

$$(1 - x)\left(1 - \frac{mx}{A}\right)\left(1 - \frac{x}{mA}\right)$$
$$+ s\left[1 - x\left(1 + \frac{m + 1/m}{A}\right) + x^2\left(\frac{1}{A} + \frac{1}{A^2}\right)\right] = 0 \qquad (2)$$

There exist, in general, three resonance frequencies which we designate in decreasing order by ω_I, ω_{II}, ω_{III}.* Equation (2) is

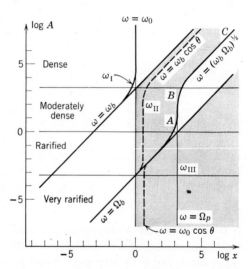

Fig. 8.1. Resonance frequencies in cold plasmas.

discussed in Appendix 5. Here we content ourselves with quoting results and illustrating them by use of Fig. 8.1 and Table 8.1. Figure 8.1 shows how the resonance frequencies vary as a function of the plasma density or A. The abscissa is $x' = \log x$, where $x = \omega_0^2/\omega_{res}^2$, and the ordinate is the value of $\log A$.

---

* This designation is not to be confused with ω_1, ω_2 previously introduced.

Table 8.1. Resonance frequencies in cold plasmas*

Resonances:	ω_{I}	ω_{II}		ω_{III}
Propagation:	θ arbitrary	$\tan^2 \theta \ll m$	$\theta = \pi/2$	$\tan^2 \theta \ll m$
Plasmas				
Very rarified	ω_b	Ω_b	Ω_b	$\omega_0 \cos \theta$
Rarified	ω_b	$\omega_0 \cos \theta$	Ω_b (4)	Ω_b
Moderately dense	ω_b (7)	$\omega_0 \cos \theta$ (8)	Ω_p (4)	Ω_b
Dense	ω_0	$\omega_b \cos \theta$	$\sqrt{\omega_b \Omega_b}$	Ω_b

* The numbers inscribed in the table refer to the formulas in the text in the transition regions.

b. Longitudinal propagation. For the case of longitudinal propagation, the three resonance frequencies are ω_0, ω_b, and Ω_b. In this mode of propagation there is no coupling between the three fundamental frequencies. We recall that the order of these three frequencies depends on the plasma density. For example, in dense plasmas $\omega_{\mathrm{I}} = \omega_0$, (see Fig. 8.1) and $\omega_{\mathrm{I}} = \omega_b$ in the other categories.

c. Transverse propagation. In the case of transverse propagation, there are only two resonance frequencies ($\omega_{\mathrm{III}} = 0$). They are given exactly in Eq. (A5.10), or neglecting terms of higher order in $1/m$ by

$$\omega_{\mathrm{I}}^2 = \omega_0^2 + \omega_b^2 \tag{3}$$

$$\omega_{\mathrm{II}}^2 = [(A + 1)/(A + m)]\, \omega_b \Omega_b \tag{4}$$

For rarified and very rarified plasmas, we see that

$$\omega_{\mathrm{I}} \simeq \omega_b$$

$$\omega_{\mathrm{II}} \simeq \Omega_b$$

The coupling between the plasma and cyclotron resonances is negligible.

In contrast, for dense and moderately dense plasmas, there is in effect coupling between the three types of resonances. The results become:

For moderately dense plasmas

$$\omega_{\mathrm{I}} \simeq \omega_b \qquad \omega_{\mathrm{II}} \simeq \omega_0/(m)^{1/2} = \Omega_? \tag{5}$$

For dense plasmas

$$\omega_{\mathrm{I}} \simeq \omega_0 \qquad \omega_{\mathrm{II}} \simeq (\omega_b \Omega_b)^{1/2} \tag{6}$$

d. Oblique propagation. In the case of oblique propagation, each resonance frequency takes on a value intermediate between extremes at $\theta = 0$ (longitudinal) and $\theta = \pi/2$ (transverse). This results from the form of Eq. (2) with which we can divide the xy plane into regimes. In Fig. 8.1 the shadowed areas are those in which the three resonances, ω_{I}, ω_{II}, and ω_{III}, are located.

In the case where the resonance frequencies are equal for both $\theta = 0$ and $\theta = \pi/2$, the results are obvious: we can say that the coupling is negligible for all θ. Thus

$\omega_{\mathrm{I}} \cong \omega_b$ for very rarified, rarified, and moderately dense plasmas.

$\omega_{\mathrm{I}} \cong \omega_0$ for dense plasmas.

$\omega_{\mathrm{II}} \cong \Omega_b$ for very rarified plasmas.

In other regions, we obtain the following approximate equations, provided that θ is not too close to $\pi/2$ (more exactly, for $\tan^2\theta \ll m$) as follows:

Transition between moderately dense and dense plasmas

$$\omega_{\mathrm{I}} \simeq \tfrac{1}{2}\{\omega_0{}^2 + \omega_b{}^2 + [(\omega_0{}^2 + \omega_b{}^2)^2 - 4\omega_0{}^2\omega_b{}^2 \cos^2 \theta]^{1/2}\} \tag{7}$$

$$\omega_{\mathrm{II}} \simeq \tfrac{1}{2}\{\omega_0{}^2 + \omega_b{}^2 - [(\omega_0{}^2 + \omega_b{}^2)^2 - 4\omega_0{}^2\omega_b{}^2 \cos^2 \theta]^{1/2}\} \tag{8}$$

Moderately dense plasmas

$$\omega_{\mathrm{II}} \simeq \omega_0 \cos \theta \tag{9}$$

Dense plasmas

$$\omega_{\mathrm{II}} \simeq \omega_b \cos \theta \tag{10}$$

Very rarified plasmas

$$\omega_{\mathrm{III}} \simeq \omega_0 \cos \theta \tag{11}$$

Rarified, moderately dense, and dense plasmas

$$\omega_{\mathrm{III}} \simeq \Omega_b \tag{12}$$

The regions of validity of the above formulas are clear in Fig. 8.1. Equations (9) and (11) are valid in part of the rarified plasma region. In addition, Eq. (7) is valid even when θ approaches $\pi/2$, since it then yields Eq. (3). The dashed curve, drawn in Fig. 8.1 as an example, corresponds to $\theta = \pi/3$.

We note that the condition $\tan^2\theta = m$ implies that, for a proton and electron plasma, $\theta = 88° 40'$. Equations (7) to (12) are thus valid even when the propagation is very nearly transverse. The domain of their validity ($\tan^2\theta \ll m$) includes directions of propagation which deviate a good bit from the orientation of the magnetic field!

In Fig. 8.1 we can observe that the resonance frequencies are related to the characteristic plasma frequencies by very simple relations. These relations are valid for a wide range of values of A. Expressions for the resonance frequencies are shown in Table 8.1. The numbers inscribed in the table refer to the formulas in the text which are valid in the corresponding transition regions.

8.3   Horizontal Asymptotes: Magnetodynamic Waves

The general formulas discussed in Chapters 6 and 9 show that the retarded wave y_1, in this case, disappears to infinity and that the other two are given by the equations

$$y_2 = \epsilon_a (1 + s) = \epsilon_a/\cos^2 \theta \qquad (13)$$

$$y_3 = \epsilon_a \qquad (14)$$

8.4   Identification of the Modes

Since the equation in u is here of second degree, there are but two waves at each frequency in cold plasmas. It is of interest to study the relation of these two waves to the four modes of propagation which exist in the general treatment. The dispersion diagram for cold plasma should naturally be obtainable from Fig. 6.4 by going to the limit $\epsilon_e = \epsilon_i = 0$. As we proceed to this limit, the points A and B and the horizontal asymptote which corresponds to y_1

disappear to infinity. This also happens to several arcs in Fig. 6.4. When $\epsilon_s \gg \epsilon_a$, the dispersion curve for each mode becomes, in the general case, two sections: one section where y is of order unity or of ϵ_a (v_ϕ is of order c or V_a) and another section where y is of order ϵ_e or ϵ_i (v_ϕ is of order V_e or V_s). The transition from one of these domains to the other occurs in a rather rapid fashion in a small frequency interval. We say that this transition region constitutes a pseudo-resonance (arc AA' in Fig. 8.2). We have come across the pseudo-resonances in transverse propagation (see Fig. 7.2). They are even more graphic in the case of longitudinal propagation (for

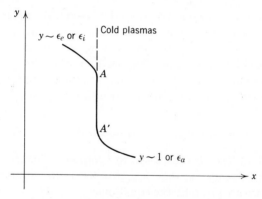

Fig. 8.2.

example, arc UU' in Fig. 7.2). Experimentally, these pseudo-resonances are very important; they can cause a change in the index of refraction by a factor of several orders of magnitude even in relatively hot plasmas.

As the plasma becomes colder, the whole upper branch, situated beyond pseudo-resonances, moves to infinity (see Fig. 8.2), and the pseudo-resonance becomes a true resonance.* Figure 8.3 shows

---

*One might note that figures such as Fig. 8.2 are very misleading: the bend of the dispersion curve at A', where the pseudo-resonance disappears, is real. On the other hand, the bend at A comes from the particular coordinates which we have chosen. This does not, however, change the line of our reasoning.

schematically where these pseudo-resonances occur in the general dispersion diagram. The shadowed regions disappear to infinity when ϵ_e and ϵ_i become large. The dispersion curves for cold plasma have the appearance shown in Fig. 8.4. Each of the modes exists only in a limited frequency region.

Figure 8.5 shows the dispersion curves of a cold plasma computed exactly for $A = 100$. The continuous lines are for longitudinal

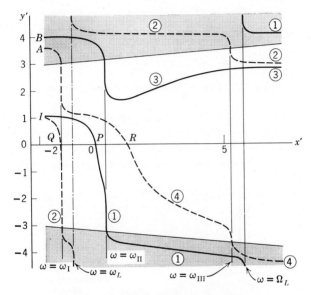

Fig. 8.3. Pseudoresonances in hot plasmas.

propagation, while the dashes are for transverse propagation. This figure is shown as an example and may be compared to the corresponding curves given in Figs. 6.8 and 7.2, which describe a plasma of temperature $T = 10,000°\,\mathrm{K}$ (plasma P_3). We observe that these curves differ only in the regions which are shadowed in Fig. 6.8 and which represent values of $y > 10^3$. This is also the case for the other plasma groups. For those we refer the reader to Figs. 6.6, 6.7, 6.9, and 6.10 in which we have also shadowed the areas where the cold plasma approximation is not valid.

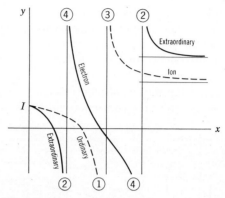

Fig. 8.4. Dispersion diagram for cold plasmas.

Numerical computations verify the qualitative statements made at the beginning of this chapter concerning the relatively large region of validity of the cold plasma approximation. We must underscore the significance of this property because the theory for

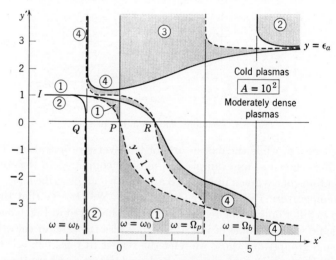

Fig. 8.5. Dispersion diagram for moderately dense, cold, plasmas;
(—) longitudinal, (- - -) transverse propagation.

cold plasmas is immune to the most important criticisms which can be expressed with regard to the general theory developed in this book and which are directed principally at the form used for the pressure tensor.

8.5 Transverse Propagation

In cold as in hot plasmas, transverse propagation is also a singular case: the line $y = 1 - x$ is then part of the dispersion curve. The rest of the curve is a cubic equation

$$y - 1 = - x\,[1 - x(1 + 1/A)]/(1 - x/x_I)\,(1 - x/x_{II}) \quad (15)$$

Where x_I and x_{II} symbolize the two resonance frequencies defined in Section 8.2 (in this case, the third resonance frequency, ω_{III}, is zero). The dispersion diagram has the appearance of Fig. 8.6.

8.6 High Frequency Approximation: Appleton-Hartree Equation

When we are interested in the propagation at frequencies larger than Ω_p, Ω_L, and Ω_T, we can simplify the cold plasma approximation by setting $\Omega_p = \Omega_L = \Omega_T = 0$. This is the Appleton-Hartree ap-

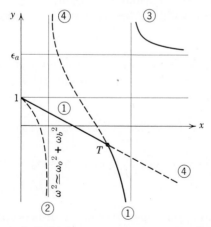

Fig. 8.6. Cold plasmas; transverse propagation.

proximation. The results can obviously be obtained from the more general theory by letting m approach infinity. However, the parameter

$$A = \omega_0^2/\omega_b\Omega_b = m\omega_0^2/\omega_b^2 \tag{16}$$

should, a priori, be considered as of order m. Thus in the Appleton-Hartree approximation we study only moderately dense plasmas ($1 \ll A < m$) or dense plasmas ($1 \ll m < A$). The computations for this approximation are carried out in Appendix 5 (Section A5.4). Here are the results:

The equation in u is

$$\left[(1 - x)\left(1 - \frac{\omega_L^2}{\omega^2}\right) - \frac{\omega_T^2}{\omega^2}\right] u^2$$
$$+ 2\left(1 - x - \frac{\omega_T^2}{2\omega^2}\right) ux + x^2(1 - x) = 0 \tag{17}$$

The dispersion curve is of fourth degree. It possesses two vertical asymptotes. The properties of the resonance frequencies ω_I and ω_{II} can be more or less represented by Fig. 8.1 provided that the region which corresponds to ω_{III}, as well as the arc ABC, is pushed to infinity toward the bottom and to the right.

There exist two parabolic branches whose equation is

$$y \simeq \pm (\omega_0/\omega_L)(x)^{1/2} \tag{18}$$

Transverse propagation constitutes, as usual, a singular case. The dispersion curve then breaks up into line IP and the hyperbola whose equation is

$$(y - 1)\left(1 - \frac{\omega_0^2 + \omega_b^2}{\omega^2}\right) + x(1 - x) = 0. \tag{19}$$

The oblique asymptote of this hyperbola is expressed by

$$y = 1 + [Am/(A + m)^2] - Ax/(A + m) \tag{20}$$

Figure 8.7 shows the appearance of the dispersion diagram for a moderately dense plasma for $\theta = 0$, $0 < \theta < \pi/2$, and $\theta = \pi/2$.

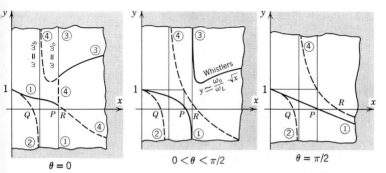

Fig. 8.7. Appleton-Hartree approximation; moderately dense plasmas.

The shadowed regions are those where the Appleton-Hartree approximation is no longer valid. Attention should be given to the parabolic branch which explains the properties of a certain type of atmospheric interference known as atmospheric whistlers [21].

The dispersion equation was published by Appleton and Hartree using a slightly different notation. Since their notation is common, it would be useful to establish a correspondence to ours. Let us set

$$T = \omega_T^2/2\omega(1 - x) \tag{21}$$

The solutions of Eq. (17) can then be written as (see Appendix 5, Section A5.4)

$$y = 1 - \frac{\omega_p^2}{\omega[\omega - T \pm (\omega_L^2 + T^2)^{1/2}]} \tag{22}$$

In addition, we can show, referring to Table 2.2 that in the case of nonzero collision frequencies ν and ν_{en}, Eqs. (21) and (23) become [see Ref. 19]

$$T = \omega_T^2/2\omega(1 - x - j\nu_1/\omega) \tag{23}$$

$$y = 1 - \frac{\omega_p^2}{\omega[\omega - j\nu_1 - T \pm (\omega_L^2 + T^2)^{1/2}]} \tag{24}$$

where

$$\nu_1 = \nu + \nu_{en} \tag{25}$$

8.7   Polarization of the Waves

a. **General properties of transverse polarization.** The general orthogonality relations of the two modes a and b, established in Chapter 6, become

$$E_{xa} E_{xb}^* + (jE_{ya}) (jE_{yb})^* = 0 \tag{26}$$

In the case of cold plasmas, the last two terms disappear since V_e and V_i are zero. We could rewrite Eq. (26) assuming that E_{xa} and E_{xb} are real; jE_{ya} and jE_{yb} are then also real (Chapter 6). We therefore have

$$E_{xa} E_{xb} - E_{ya} E_{yb} = 0 \tag{27}$$

or

$$(E_{ya}/E_{xa}) (E_{yb}/E_{xb}) = 1 \tag{28}$$

Since the two ratios E_{ya}/E_{xa} and E_{yb}/E_{xb} are imaginary, Eq. (28) shows that the transverse polarization of the two waves which exist at a given frequency in a cold plasma are represented by two symmetric ellipses whose axes are the spatial x and y axes. These ellipses are described in opposite directions (see Fig. 8.8.) From what we have seen in Chapters 3 and 7, these two ellipses become circles for the case of longitudinal propagation and flatten out to give linear polarization for transverse propagation.

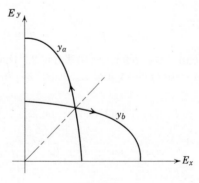

Fig. 8.8.

b. High frequency case: Appleton-Hartree approximation.
The Appleton-Hartree equation can be written using the following
values from Eq. (A2.11)

$$P = L = T = 1/\epsilon_e = 1/\epsilon_i = 0$$

Multiplying all the terms by $1 - l^2$ and changing the signs in the
second row and second column, we obtain

$$\begin{vmatrix} (1 - l^2)(1 - y) - x & xl & -pl \\ xl & (1 - l^2)(1 - y) - x & pll \\ -pl & pll & (1 - l^2)(1 - x) - l^2 \end{vmatrix} = 0 \quad (29)$$

The variables which correspond to the three columns are E_x, E_y/j,
and $v_{ez}m_e\omega_p/q_e$. By forming the ratio of the third row minors
corresponding to the variables E_x and E_y/j, we obtain

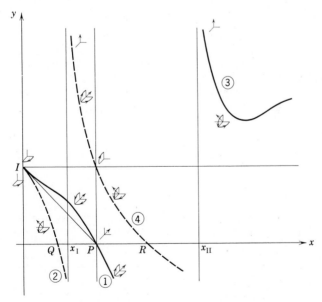

Fig. 8.9. Appleton-Hartree approximation: polarization of waves.

$$E_y/jE_x = - l(1 - y)/(1 - y - x) \qquad (30)$$

By forming the ratio of the minors in the first row corresponding to the variables E_y/j and $v_{ez}m_e\omega_p/q_e$, we obtain, considering Eq. (A4.5),

$$E_z/E_y = - (l/l)(1 - y - x)/(1 - x) \qquad (31)$$

These two equations are useful in the detailed study of the polarization of the waves. The results are shown in Fig. 8.9 and in Table 8.2.

Table 8.2. Wave polarization in the high frequency region

x	0		x_{I}		1		x_{II}		∞
ω	∞		ω_{I}		ω_0		ω_{II}		0
Modes		y_1		y_1		y_1		y_3	
E_y/jE_x	$+1$	$+$		$+$	$+\infty\|\|-\infty$	$-$	$-\omega_L/\omega_{\mathrm{II}}$	$-$	0
E_z/E_y	0	$+$		$+$	ω_T/ω_L	$+$	$+\infty\|\|-\infty$	$-$	$-\omega_T/\omega_L$
Modes		y_2		y_4		y_4		y_4	
E_y/jE_x	-1	$-$	$-\omega_L/\omega_{\mathrm{I}}$	$-$	0	$+$		$+$	0
E_z/E_y	0	$-$	$-\infty\|\|+\infty$	$+$	$+\infty\|\|-\infty$	$-$		$-$	$-\omega_T/\omega_L$

CHAPTER 9

Magnetodynamic Waves

In Chapter 6 we have seen that in the general treatment the dispersion curve exhibits three horizontal asymptotes which describe low frequency or magnetodynamic waves.* These waves possess certain properties similar to those of sound waves propagating in a neutral gas:

1. The speed of propagation is independent of the frequency.

2. During the traversal of the wave, the ions and electrons move together; space charge phenomena play only a secondary role.

In Chapters 3 and 4 we have seen two types of nondispersive and neutral waves: the transverse Alfvén wave and the longitudinal pseudosonic waves. The latter exist when the transverse component of the magnetic field is zero. Magnetodynamic waves arise from the coupling of these two waves by the transverse magnetic field. In Chapter 6 we have seen (Section 6.3 and Fig. 6.4) that these waves can be considered the limit (as ω goes to zero) of the ordinary mode y_1, the extraordinary mode y_2, and the ionic mode y_3; the corresponding magnetodynamic waves are ordered in increasing velocity. The electron mode y_4, which has an oblique asymptote, is always evanescent as $\omega \to 0$.

9.1 Speeds of Propagation

a. **General equations; oblique Alfvén wave and magnetoacoustic waves.** The speeds of propagation of magnetodynamic

---

*See footnote on page 17.

re obtained from the indices of refraction computed in
..pter 6 (see Eqs. 6.24 and 6.25) and in Appendix 3.

$$y_2 = \epsilon_a / \cos^2 \theta \tag{1}$$

$$y_1, y_3 = \tfrac{1}{2} \left\{ \frac{\epsilon_a + \epsilon_s - 1}{\cos^2 \theta} + 1 \right.$$

$$\left. + \epsilon \sqrt{\left(\frac{\epsilon_a + \epsilon_s - 1}{\cos^2 \theta} - 1 \right)^2 - \frac{4(\epsilon_a - 1)(\epsilon_s - 1)}{\cos^2 \theta}} \right\} \tag{2}$$

Thus

$$V_2^2 = c^2/y_2 = V_a^2 \cos^2 \theta \tag{3}$$

$$V_1^2, \ V_3^2 = \frac{V_a^2}{2} + \frac{V_s^2}{2} - \frac{V_a^2 V_s^2}{2c^2} \sin^2 \theta$$

$$- \frac{\epsilon}{2} \left\{ \left[V_a^2 + V_s^2 - \frac{V_a^2 V_s^2}{c^2} (1 + \cos^2 \theta) \right]^2 \right.$$

$$\left. - 4 V_a^2 V_s^2 \left(1 - \frac{V_a^2}{c^2} \right) \left(1 - \frac{V_s^2}{c^2} \right) \cos^2 \theta \right\}^{\frac{1}{2}} \tag{4}$$

ϵ is taken as $+1$ for the y_1 mode and -1 for the y_3 mode. We easily
verify that

$$y_1 \geq y_2 \geq y_3 \qquad \text{or equivalently: } V_1 \leq V_2 \leq V_3 \tag{5}$$

The extraordinary wave y_2 can be distinguished from the other
two by its speed V_2, which is independent of ϵ_s. The thermal motion
in the medium plays no role in its propagation. The speed of this
"oblique Alfvén wave" satisfies the relation

$$\frac{c^2}{V_2^2} = \frac{c^2}{V_a^2 \cos^2 \theta} = \frac{1 + A}{\cos^2 \theta} = \frac{1}{\cos^2 \theta} + \frac{\omega_0^2}{\omega_L \Omega_L} \tag{6}$$

Referring to Chapter 3, we note that for longitudinal propagation this wave is equivalent to one of the components of the transverse Alfvén wave. The other component of the Alfvén wave is
identified with one of the two waves y_1 or y_3 (i.e., with the ordinary
or ionic modes) depending on whether V_a is larger or smaller than
V_s. This matter will be clarified in the following section. The speed

V_2 depends solely on the longitudinal component of the magnetic field and becomes zero with it in transverse propagation.

The ordinary wave y_1 and the ionic wave y_3 have speeds which depend on the thermal motion in the medium. We shall designate them as magnetoacoustic waves; y_1 is the retarded magnetoacoustic wave and y_3 the accelerated magnetoacoustic wave.

b. Propagation speed as a function of the propagation angle. The variation of V_2 as a function of the angle of propagation ϑ is clear from Eq. (3). The behavior of the magnetoacoustic wave speeds V_1 and V_2, as a function of ϵ_a, ϵ_s, and θ, is obtained from Eq. (A3.23) which, with the aid of the substitution $s = \tan^2\theta$, becomes

$$[y - 1 - (\epsilon_a - 1)(1 + s)] [y - \epsilon_s] - s(y - 1) \epsilon_s = 0 \qquad (7)$$

Equation (2) stems from the above equation. The representative curve $y(s) = 0$ is a hyperbola. There exists a distinction between confined plasmas ($\epsilon_a < \epsilon_s$) or unconfined plasmas ($\epsilon_a > \epsilon_s$); the corresponding hyperbolas are shown in Figs. 9.1 and 9.2. The wave y_1 is represented by the upper branches, and y_3 by the lower branches of those hyperbolas. The points where the asymptotes intercept the y axis are

$$\epsilon_1 = \epsilon_a + \epsilon_s - 1 + (\epsilon_a - 1)(\epsilon_s - 1)/(\epsilon_a + \epsilon_s - 1) \qquad (8)$$

$$\epsilon_3 = \epsilon_a\epsilon_s/(\epsilon_a + \epsilon_s - 1) \qquad (9)$$

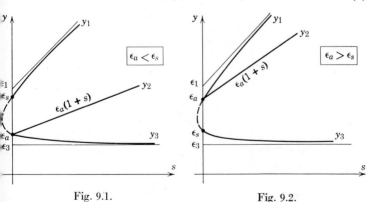

Fig. 9.1.   Fig. 9.2.

Behavior of y_1, y_2, y_3 as a function of the propagation angle ($s = \tan^2\theta$).

The equations for these asymptotes are

$$y = (\epsilon_a + \epsilon_s - 1)s + \epsilon_1 \qquad \text{and } y = \epsilon_3$$

Also drawn in Figs. 9.1 and 9.2 are the lines $y = \epsilon_a(1 + s)$ which show the variation of y_2 with the variable s.

The waves y_1 and y_3 behave differently as θ grows; y_3 tends to a limit ϵ_3, which means that the speed of propagation of the ion mode becomes virtually independent of θ. On the other hand, y_1 behaves in the following manner as θ increases:

$$(\epsilon_a + \epsilon_s - 1)/\cos^2 \theta$$

Hence the speed V_1, as well as V_2, is proportional to $\cos \theta$ and approaches zero in the case of transverse propagation. When ϵ_a and ϵ_s differ greatly, asymptotic behavior is approached for small values of θ.

These figures illustrate that the two modes which approach the Alfvén waves ($y = \epsilon_a$) as $\theta \to 0$ are the modes y_2, and y_3 when $\epsilon_s > \epsilon_a$, and y_1 and y_2 if $\epsilon_s < \epsilon_a$.

For the usual plasmas, dense or moderately dense, V_a and V_s are always much smaller than the speed of light, and we can express Eq. (4) in the following simplified form

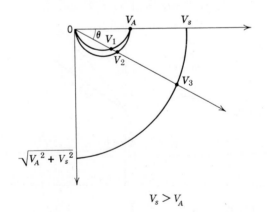

$$V_s > V_A$$

Fig. 9.3.

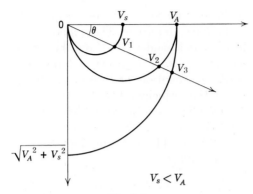

Fig. 9.4.

$$V_1^2, \; V_3^2 = \tfrac{1}{2}\{V_a^2 + V_s^2 - \epsilon[(V_a^2 + V_s^2)^2 - 4V_a^2 V_s^2 \cos^2\theta]^{1/2}\} \quad (10)$$

The velocities in a polar representation are drawn in Figs. 9.3 and 9.4.

9.2 Polarization of Magnetodynamic Waves

We shall borrow general formulas from Appendix 4 to study the polarization of magnetodynamic waves. We seek to find the solution of these formulas in the limit of low frequencies. The computations [18] lead to the following results

$$\frac{E_x}{a} = -\frac{\omega_p^2}{\omega^2}\left(y - \frac{\epsilon_a}{\cos^2\theta}\right)\left(\frac{y}{\epsilon_s} - \frac{1}{\cos^2\theta}\right) + O\,(1) \qquad (11)$$

$$\frac{jE_y}{a} = \frac{\omega_p^2}{\omega_L\omega}\tan^2\theta\left(\frac{1}{\epsilon_e} - \frac{1}{\epsilon_i}\right)y$$
$$+ \frac{\omega_0^2\omega_p^2}{\omega_L\omega}\left(\frac{1}{\omega_L^2} - \frac{1}{\Omega_L^2}\right)\left(\frac{y}{\epsilon_s} - \frac{1}{\cos^2\theta}\right) + O(\omega) \qquad (12)$$

$$\frac{m_e\omega_p}{q_e}\frac{v_{ez}}{a} = -\frac{\omega_0^2}{\omega^2}\frac{\omega_p}{\omega_L}\tan\theta\left(y - \frac{\epsilon_a}{\cos^2\theta}\right) + O(1) \qquad (13)$$

$$\frac{m_i\Omega_p}{q_i}\frac{v_{iz}}{a} = \frac{\omega_0^2}{\omega^2}\frac{\Omega_p}{\Omega_L}\tan\theta\left(y - \frac{\epsilon_a}{\cos^2\theta}\right) + O(1) \qquad (14)$$

In these formulas a is an arbitrary coefficient of proportionality which defines the wave amplitude. The symbol $O(1)$ represents all the terms which are independent of ω, and the symbol $O(\omega)$ represents ω-dependent terms. The principal terms in these expressions are in $1/\omega^2$. The equation for E_y is an exception: the leading term is $1/\omega$. All the principal $1/\omega^2$ terms become zero when $y - \epsilon_a/\cos^2 \theta = 0$ (oblique Alfvén waves). These terms are not zero for the accelerated or retarded magnetoacoustic waves. Finally, combining Eqs. (13) and (14), and using Eq. (2.17), the $1/\omega^2$ terms cancel out exactly in all cases:

$$E_z/a = O(1/\omega) \tag{15}$$

a. Polarization of the oblique Alfvén wave. Setting $y = \epsilon_a/\cos^2 \theta$, the preceding equations may be written

$$\frac{E_x}{O(1)} = \frac{jE_y}{O(1/\omega)} = \frac{m_e\omega_p v_{ez}/q_e}{O(1)} = \frac{m_i\Omega_p v_{iz}/q_i}{O(1)} = \frac{jE_z}{O(1/\omega)} \tag{16}$$

The field E_x is negligible with respect to E_y and E_z. The electric field of the Alfvén wave is therefore contained in the $(\mathbf{B}_0, \mathbf{k})$ plane and, consequently, its magnetic field is directed along the x axis and is equal to

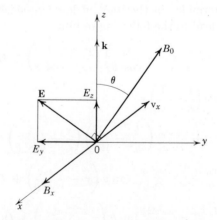

Fig. 9.5. Polarization of the oblique Alfvén wave.

$$B_x = - [\epsilon_a^{1/2}/c \cos \theta] E_y \qquad (17)$$

The vector diagram is shown in Fig. 9.5.

To describe the structure of the wave, we study the particle velocities by making use of the momentum transfer equations, Eqs. (2.22)–(2.24). Neglecting collisions, we have

$$E_x + v_{ey}B_L - v_{ez}B_T - j\omega m_e v_{ex}/q_e = 0 \qquad (18)$$

$$E_y - v_{ex}B_L - j\omega m_e v_{ey}/q_e = 0 \qquad (19)$$

$$E_z + v_{ex}B_T - [j\omega m_e v_{ez}/q_e] [1 - (\epsilon_a/\epsilon_e \cos^2 \theta)] = 0 \qquad (20)$$

From Eq. (20) we obtain, with the use of Eqs. (13) and (15),

$$\begin{aligned} \frac{v_{ex}}{v_{ez}} &= -\frac{1}{B_T}\frac{E_z}{v_{ez}} - j\frac{\omega}{\omega_T}\left(1 - \frac{\epsilon_a}{\epsilon_e \cos^2 \theta}\right) \\ &= O\left(\frac{1}{\omega}\right) - j\frac{\omega}{\omega_T}\left(1 - \frac{\epsilon_a}{\epsilon_a \cos^2 \theta}\right) \end{aligned} \qquad (21)$$

and from Eq. (18),

$$v_{ey}/v_{ez} = \tan \theta + O(1) \qquad (22)$$

Equation (22) shows that v_{ey} and v_{ez} are of the same order. Equation (21), where the second term is negligible, shows that v_{ex} is of order $1/\omega$ with respect to v_{ez}, and also, therefore, with respect to v_{ey}. The results for ion motion are analogous, and hence the particle motion occurs entirely along the x axis. Equation (19) and the analogous equation for ions show that

$$v_{ex} = v_{ix} = E_y/B_L \qquad (23)$$

The ions and the electrons accompany each other in their motion. The whole fluid mass vibrates perpendicularly to the direction of propagation. We can here reiterate the remarks made at the end of Chapter 3 for the purely transverse Alfvén wave.

From Eqs. (19) and (20) one finds

$$E_z = - E_y\tan \theta \qquad (24)$$

The electric field is perpendicular to $\mathbf{B}_0$. The longitudinal component of this electric field, which appears when B_T is not zero, and the corresponding space charge are both caused by charge displacements which are extremely small with respect to the transverse displacement. These displacements play no role in propagation.

b. Polarization of the accelerated and retarded magneto-acoustic waves. For the magnetodynamic waves y_1 and y_3, the terms in $1/\omega^2$ from Eqs. (11), (13), and (14) do not vanish. Therefore

$$\frac{E_x}{-\dfrac{1}{\epsilon_s}\left(y - \dfrac{\epsilon_a}{\cos^2\theta}\right)\left(y - \dfrac{\epsilon_s}{\cos^2\theta}\right)\dfrac{\omega_0^2}{\omega^2}} = \frac{jE_y}{O(1/\omega)}$$

$$= \frac{-4\pi\bar{n}_e q_e v_{ez}}{\tan\theta\left(y - \dfrac{\epsilon_a}{\cos^2\theta}\right)\dfrac{\omega_0^2\omega_p}{\omega_L\omega^2} + O\,(1)} \qquad (25)$$

$$= \frac{4\pi\bar{n}_i q_i v_{iz}}{\tan\theta\left(y - \dfrac{\epsilon_a}{\cos^2\theta}\right)\dfrac{\omega_0^2\Omega_p}{\Omega_L\omega^2} + O(1)} = \frac{jE_z}{O\left(\dfrac{1}{\omega}\right)}$$

These equations show that E_y and E_z (of order $1/\omega$) are negligible with respect to E_x (of order of $1/\omega^2$). The electric field of the wave is directed along the x axis, and the magnetic field $B_y = E_x/V$ is directed along the y axis (Fig. 9.6). V is the wave speed.

The particle motion is confined to the yz plane. Equation (25) shows that, to second order,

$$v_{ez} = v_{iz} \qquad (26)$$

From Eq. (2.24), one obtains

$$v_{ex}/v_{ez} = -\,(E_z/B_T v_{ez}) - j\,(\omega/\omega_T)\,[1 - (V_e^2/V^2)] \qquad (27)$$

From Eq. (25), E_z/v_{ez} is of order ω; therefore the ratio v_{ex}/v_{ez} is also of the same order. From Eq. (2.24) we see that this is also the case for the ratio v_{ix}/v_{iz}. Hence the particle velocity components along the x axis are negligible (see Fig. 9.6).

We now compute the ratio v_{ey}/v_{ez} with the help of Eq. (2.22). Neglecting v_{ex}/v_{ez}, this equation gives

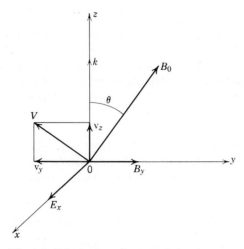

Fig. 9.6. Polarization of magnetoacoustic waves.

$$v_{ey}/v_{ez} = (B_T/B_L) - (E_x/B_L v_{ez}) = \tan \theta - (E_x/B_L v_{ez}) \quad (28)$$

Equations (25) lead to

$$E_x/B_L v_{ez} = - (1/\epsilon_s \tan \theta) [y - (\epsilon_s/\cos^2 \theta)] \quad (29)$$

and

$$v_{ey}/v_{ez} = (1/\tan \theta) (V_s^2/V^2 - 1) \quad (30)$$

The same ratio is obtained for v_{iy}/v_{iz}, starting from Eq. (2.22′). Consequently

$$v_e = v_i$$

The ions and the electrons accompany each other in their motion, and the waves remain neutral to the same order of approximation as the pseudosonic waves in Chapter 4.

Equation (30) shows that the slope of the velocity with respect to the direction propagation is a function of the ratio V_s/V. This slope will be quite different for the modes y_1 and y_3 and takes on simple values when V_a and V_s differ greatly in magnitude.

1. $V_s \gg V_a$

The ion mode y_3, or accelerated mode, has a speed $V = V_s$ according to Eq. (10), and $v_{ey} = v_{iy} = 0$ from Eq. (30). The particle motion is in the direction of propagation. This wave is not very different from the pseudosonic waves studied in Chapter 4.

The ordinary mode, or retarded wave y_1, has a speed

$$V \sim V_a \cos \theta \ll V_s$$

and consequently $v_{ey} \gg v_{ez}$. This wave is purely transverse and does not differ much from the oblique Alfvén wave. In this case, the longitudinal and transverse modes do not couple to each other.

2. $V_a \gg V_s$

The mode y_3 has a speed $V = V_a \cos \theta$ and from Eq. (30)

$$v_{ey}/v_{ez} = -1/\tan \theta \tag{31}$$

This accelerated wave, which we have described as an ion wave, resembles, in this case, an Alfvén wave; its speed depends essentially on the magnetic field. However, the motion of the fluid, instead of being perpendicular to the direction of propagation as in the case of the Alfvén wave, is normal to the magnetic field $\mathbf{B}_0$, as seen in Eq. (31).

The ordinary mode y_1 has a speed $V = V_s \cos \theta$ and

$$v_{ey}/v_{ez} = \tan \theta \tag{32}$$

Table 9.1

	$V_s \gg V_a$		$V_s \ll V_a$	
	V	v	V	v
y_1	$V_a \cos \theta$	$\perp \mathbf{k}$	$V_s \cos \theta$	$\parallel \mathbf{B}_0$
y_2	$V_a \cos \theta$	$\perp \mathbf{B}_0, \mathbf{k}$	$V_a \cos \theta$	$\perp \mathbf{B}_0, \mathbf{k}$
y_3	V_s	$\parallel \mathbf{k}$	V_a	$\perp \mathbf{B}_0$

This wave resembles a sound wave because its speed depends essentially on the compressibility of the medium. However, the motion of the fluid, instead of being parallel to the direction of propagation, is, according to Eq. (22), parallel to the magnetic field.

The above results are summarized in Table 9.1.

We find, in all the magnetodynamic waves, that the ion and electron speeds are equal. The plasma behaves as a conducting homogeneous fluid. Had we assumed this result a priori, we would have obtained directly some of the conclusions which we have derived [6]. One can show [2] that the motion of the medium can be described by two macroscopic equations:

$$\rho(\partial \mathbf{v}/\partial t) = \mathbf{j} \times \mathbf{B} - \nabla p \text{ (equation of motion)}$$

$$\mathbf{E} + \mathbf{v} \times \mathbf{B} = 0 \text{ (Ohm's law)}$$

where $\mathbf{v}$ is the velocity of the fluid and p the total pressure. From these equations we deduce the polarizations of the three modes.

c. **Energies.** The general relation, Eq. (5. 26), is

$$W_M + W_P = W_E + W_K \tag{33}$$

In the case of the oblique Alfvén wave, $W_P = 0$, and the magnetic energy is always equal to the sum of the electrical and kinetic energies. The results of the preceding section, Eqs. (17), (24), and (23), allow us to write

$$W_M = \frac{E^2}{8\pi} = \frac{F_y{}^2}{8\pi c^2} y = \frac{E_y{}^2}{8\pi c^2} \frac{\epsilon_a}{\cos^2 \theta} \tag{34}$$

$$W_E = \frac{E^2}{8\pi c^2} = \frac{E_y{}^2 + E_z{}^2}{8\pi c^2} = \frac{E_y{}^2}{8\pi c^2} \cdot \frac{1}{\cos^2 \theta} \tag{35}$$

$$W_K = \tfrac{1}{2}(\bar{n}_e m_e + \bar{n}_i m_i)\mathbf{v}_{ex}{}^2 = \frac{E_y{}^2}{8\pi c^2} \cdot \frac{4\pi \rho c^2}{B_L{}^2} = \frac{E_y{}^2}{8\pi c^2} \frac{\epsilon_a - 1}{\cos^2 \theta} \tag{36}$$

In the rarified plasmas ($\epsilon_a \simeq 1$), the kinetic energy is negligible. In dense and moderately dense plasmas ($\epsilon_a \gg 1$), the electrical energy, in contrast, is negligible, and equipartition exists between the magnetic and kinetic energies. This property is characteristic of the behavior of Alfvén waves in the usual plasmas.

In the case of retarded or accelerated magnetoacoustic waves,

$$W_M = E_x^2/8\pi V^2 = (E_x^2/8\pi c^2)\, y \tag{37}$$

$$W_E = E_x^2/8\pi c^2 \tag{38}$$

$$W_K = \tfrac{1}{2}\rho(v_{ez}^2 + v_{ey}^2) = \tfrac{1}{2}\rho v_{ez}^2\,[1 + (v_{ey}^2/v_{ez}^2)] \tag{39}$$

$$W_P = \tfrac{1}{2}\rho(V_s^2/V^2)\,v_{ez}^2 = \tfrac{1}{2}\rho(y/\epsilon_s)\,v_{ez}^2 \tag{40}$$

From Eqs. (7), (29), and (30), we can verify the equipartition relation, Eq. (33). Moreover, we can write

$$\frac{W_E}{W_K} = \frac{E_x^2}{B_L^2 v_{ez}^2} \cdot \frac{B_L^2}{4\pi\rho c^2}\frac{1}{1 + v_{ey}^2/v_{ez}^2} \tag{41}$$

$$= a\,\frac{\cos^2\theta}{(\epsilon_a - 1)\,(1 + v_{ey}^2/v_{ez}^2)}$$

$$\frac{W_M}{W_P} = \frac{E_x^2}{B_L^2 v_{ez}^2} \cdot \frac{B_L^2}{4\pi\rho c^2}\epsilon_s = a\,\frac{\epsilon_s \cos^2\theta}{\epsilon_a - 1} \tag{42}$$

where

$$a = E_x^2/B_L^2 v_{ez}^2$$

First, let us evaluate these ratios for the accelerated wave y_3. When $V_s \gg V_a$, we have $v_{ey} = 0$ and $a = \tan^2\theta$ [27]. Thus

$$W_E/W_K = \sin^2\theta/(\epsilon_a - 1) \tag{43}$$

and

$$W_M/W_P = \epsilon_s \sin^2\theta/(\epsilon_a - 1) \tag{44}$$

When $V_s \ll V_a$,

$$v_{ey}/v_{ez} = -1/\tan\theta$$

and

$$a = 1/\cos^2\theta \tan\theta$$

Thus

$$W_E/W_K = \sin\theta\cos\theta/(\epsilon_a - 1) \tag{45}$$

and

$$W_M/W_P = \epsilon_s/(\epsilon_a - 1) \tan \theta \qquad (46)$$

For the retarded wave y_1, when $V_s \gg V_a$

$$v_{ez} = 0$$

and

$$a = (1/\sin^2 \theta) \, [(\epsilon_a/\epsilon_s) - 1]^2$$

Thus

$$W_E = W_P = 0 \qquad (47)$$

When $V_s \ll V_a$,

$$v_{ey}/v_{ez} = \tan \theta$$

and

$$a = E_x = 0$$

Thus

$$W_E = W_M = 0 \qquad (48)$$

Since, in the usual plasmas ϵ_a, $\epsilon_s \gg 1$, we see that W_E is always negligible. The accelerated wave y_3 contains both magnetic and potential energy in amounts depending upon the angle θ and the relative values of ϵ_s and ϵ_a. The retarded wave y_1 becomes either an Alfvén wave when $V_s \gg V_a$ and $W_M = W_K$ or a sound wave when $V_s \ll V_a$ and $W_P = W_K$.

In closing, we should note that the orthogonality relations, Eq. (6.4), are satisfied for the three magnetodynamic waves. First, we observe that the oblique Alfvén wave is orthogonal to the magnetoacoustic waves since the electric field and the velocities have no common component.

The orthogonality relation between the two magnetosonic waves is written as

$$E_{xa}E_{xb}/8\pi + \tfrac{1}{2} \rho \, V_s{}^2 v_{za} v_{zb} = 0 \qquad (49)$$

where v_{za} and v_{zb} are the average particle velocities along the z axis for each of the two modes.

From this we conclude that the magnetoacoustic modes are distinguished from each other by the sign of the ratio E_x/v_z, which is positive for the accelerated mode and negative for the retarded mode.

The Conductivity Tensor

A1.1 General Equations

The conductivity tensor is obtained from the momentum transport equations, Eqs. (2.22), (2.23), (2.24), (2.22'), (2.23'), and (2.24'). Setting

$$\mathbf{J}_e = \bar{n}_e q_e \mathbf{v}_e \qquad \mathbf{J}_i = \bar{n}_i q_i \mathbf{v}_i \qquad (1)$$

we can express these equations in matrix form:

$$A_e \mathbf{J}_e + (\nu/j\omega)\mathbf{J}_i = \sigma_{0e}\mathbf{E} \qquad (2)$$

$$(\nu/j\omega)\mathbf{J}_e + A_i \mathbf{J}_i = \sigma_{0e}\mathbf{E} \qquad (3)$$

where

$$\sigma_{0e} = \omega_p{}^2/4\pi c^2 j\omega \qquad \sigma_{0i} = \Omega_p{}^2/4\pi c^2 j\omega \qquad (4)$$

$$A_e = \begin{bmatrix} 1 + \dfrac{\nu + \nu_{en}}{j\omega} & -jl & jl \\[2ex] jl & 1 + \dfrac{\nu + \nu_{en}}{j\omega} & 0 \\[2ex] -jl & 0 & 1 - \dfrac{y}{\epsilon_e} + \dfrac{\nu + \nu_{en}}{j\omega} \end{bmatrix} \qquad (5)$$

$$A_i = m \begin{bmatrix} 1 + \dfrac{\nu/m + \nu_{in}}{j\omega} & jL & -jT \\[2ex] -jL & 1 + \dfrac{\nu/m + \nu_{in}}{j\omega} & 0 \\[2ex] jT & 0 & 1 - \dfrac{y}{\epsilon_i} + \dfrac{\nu/m + \nu_{in}}{j\omega} \end{bmatrix} \qquad (6)$$

113

By solving Eqs. (2) and (3), we formally obtain

$$\mathbf{J} = \sigma \mathbf{E} = (\sigma_e + \sigma_i)\mathbf{E} \tag{7}$$

where

$$\sigma_e = \left(A_i A_e + \frac{\nu^2}{\omega^2}\right)^{-1} \left(A_i - \frac{\nu}{j\omega}\right) \sigma_{0e} \tag{8}$$

$$\sigma_i = \left(A_e A_i + \frac{\nu^2}{\omega^2}\right)^{-1} \left(A_e - \frac{\nu}{j\omega}\right) \sigma_{0e} \tag{9}$$

A1.2 Case $\nu = 0$

When $\nu = 0$, we obtain from Eqs. (8) and (9)

$$\sigma_e = \sigma_e^{(0)} = A_e^{-1}\sigma_{0e} \tag{10}$$

$$\sigma_i = \sigma_i^{(0)} = A_i^{-1}\sigma_{0e} \tag{11}$$

Substituting the inverse of the matrices A_e and A_i, we get

$$
\sigma_e^{(0)} = \frac{\sigma_{0e}}{(1 - l^2)(1 - y/\epsilon_e) - l^2}
$$
$$
\times \begin{bmatrix}
1 - \dfrac{y}{\epsilon_e} & jl\left(1 - \dfrac{y}{\epsilon_e}\right) & -jl \\[2ex]
-jl\left(1 - \dfrac{y}{\epsilon_e}\right) & 1 - \dfrac{y}{\epsilon_e} - l^2 & -ll \\[2ex]
jt & -ll & 1 - l^2
\end{bmatrix} \tag{12}
$$

$$
\sigma_i^{(0)} = \frac{\sigma_{0i}}{(1 - L^2)(1 - y/\epsilon_i) - T^2}
$$
$$
\times \begin{bmatrix}
1 - \dfrac{y}{\epsilon_i} & -jL\left(1 - \dfrac{y}{\epsilon_i}\right) & jT \\[2ex]
jL\left(1 - \dfrac{y}{\epsilon_i}\right) & 1 - \dfrac{y}{\epsilon_i} - T^2 & -LT \\[2ex]
-jT & -LT & 1 - L^2
\end{bmatrix} \tag{13}
$$

A1.3   Case $\nu \neq 0$

When collisions cannot be neglected, we can compute their nth order contribution in ν/ω by successive approximations and the use of the expansions [25]

$$\sigma_e = \sigma_e^{(0)} + \frac{\nu}{\omega} \sigma_e^{(1)} + \frac{\nu^2}{\omega^2} \sigma_e^{(2)} + \cdots$$

$$\sigma_i = \sigma_i^{(0)} + \frac{\nu}{\omega} \sigma_i^{(1)} + \frac{\nu^2}{\omega^2} \sigma_i^{(2)} + \cdots \tag{14}$$

Each successive term can be computed by recursion formulas which are valid for $n \geq 1$:

$$\sigma_e^{(n)} j = \frac{\sigma_e^{(0)}}{\sigma_{0e}} \left[\alpha_e \sigma_e^{(n-1)} + \sigma_i^{(n-1)} \right]$$

$$\sigma_i^{(n)} j = \frac{\sigma_i^{(0)}}{\sigma_{0e}} \left[\alpha_e \sigma_i^{(n-1)} + \sigma_e^{(n-1)} \right] \tag{15}$$

where

$$\alpha_e = 1 + \nu_{en}/\nu \qquad \alpha_i = 1 + m\nu_{in}/\nu \tag{16}$$

For a completely ionized gas ($\nu_{en} = \nu_{in} = 0$), Eqs. (14) and (15) lead to very simple results [25]

$$\sigma = \frac{\sigma^{(0)}}{1 - j\dfrac{\nu}{\omega}\dfrac{\sigma^{(0)}}{\sigma_{0e}}} \tag{17}$$

where $\sigma^{(0)} = \sigma_e^{(0)} + \sigma_i^{(0)}$.

The Dispersion Relation as An Eigenvalue Equation ($v = v_{en} = v_{in} = 0$)

When v, v_{en}, and v_{in} are zero, we can transform the determinant of Table 2.2 into a symmetric fourth order matrix.

To simplify the writing, we set

$$p = \frac{\omega_p}{\omega}, \qquad l = \frac{\omega_L}{\omega}, \qquad t = \frac{\omega_T}{\omega}, \qquad \sqrt{\epsilon_e} = \frac{c}{V_e},$$

$$P = \frac{\Omega_p}{\omega}, \qquad L = \frac{\Omega_L}{\omega}, \qquad T = \frac{\Omega_T}{\omega}, \qquad \sqrt{\epsilon_i} = \frac{c}{V_i} \tag{1}$$

Then multiply lines (2) and (5) by p, lines (3) and (6) by P, line (8) by $p\sqrt{\epsilon_e}$, line (9) by $P\sqrt{\epsilon_i}$; and multiply columns (2) and (5) by $1/p$, columns (3) and (6) by $1/P$, column (8) by $\sqrt{\epsilon_e}/p$, and column (9) by $\sqrt{\epsilon_i}/P$. Table 2.2 then becomes Table A2.1.

In this table, we have indicated the variable which corresponds to each column.

The equation obtained by setting the determinant of Table A2.1 equal to zero resembles a matrix eigenvalue equation. Moreover, only four diagonal terms contain the unknown variable y. Hence, we shall perform a transformation into an eigenvalue equation of a fourth order matrix. First, simple permutations between lines and between columns enable us to regroup the diagonal terms which contain y. We obtain the equation

116

Table A2.1

E_x	$\dfrac{v_{ex}}{j}\dfrac{m_e\omega_p}{q_e}$	$\dfrac{v_{ix}}{j}\dfrac{m_i\Omega_p}{q_i}$	jE_y	$v_{ey}\dfrac{m_e\omega_p}{q_e}$	$v_{iy}\dfrac{m_i\Omega_p}{q_i}$	jE_z	$v_{ez}\dfrac{m_e\omega_p}{q_e\sqrt{\epsilon_e}}$	$v_{iz}\dfrac{m_i\Omega_p}{q_i\sqrt{\epsilon_i}}$
$1-y$	p	P	0	0	0	0	0	0
p	1	0	0	$-l$	0	0	$t\sqrt{\epsilon_e}$	0
P	0	1	0	0	L	0	0	$-T\sqrt{\epsilon_i}$
0	0	0	$1-y$	p	P	0	0	0
0	$-l$	0	p	1	0	0	0	0
0	0	L	P	0	1	0	0	0
0	0	0	0	0	0	1	$p\sqrt{\epsilon_e}$	$P\sqrt{\epsilon_i}$
0	$t\sqrt{\epsilon_e}$	0	0	0	0	$p\sqrt{\epsilon_e}$	ϵ_e-y	0
0	0	$-T\sqrt{\epsilon_i}$	0	0	0	$P\sqrt{\epsilon_i}$	0	ϵ_i-y

$$
\left|
\begin{array}{ccccc|cccc}
1 & 0 & -l & 0 & 0 & p & 0 & l\sqrt{\epsilon_e} & 0 \\
0 & 1 & 0 & L & 0 & P & 0 & 0 & -T\sqrt{\epsilon_i} \\
-l & 0 & 1 & 0 & 0 & 0 & p & 0 & 0 \\
0 & L & 0 & 1 & 0 & 0 & P & 0 & 0 \\
0 & 0 & 0 & 0 & 1 & 0 & 0 & p\sqrt{\epsilon_e} & P\sqrt{\epsilon_i} \\
\hline
p & P & 0 & 0 & 0 & 1-y & 0 & 0 & 0 \\
0 & 0 & p & P & 0 & 0 & 1-y & 0 & 0 \\
l\sqrt{\epsilon_e} & 0 & 0 & 0 & p\sqrt{\epsilon_e} & 0 & 0 & \epsilon_e - y & 0 \\
0 & -T\sqrt{\epsilon_i} & 0 & 0 & P\sqrt{\epsilon_i} & 0 & 0 & 0 & \epsilon_i - y
\end{array}
\right| = 0 \quad (2)
$$

This equation can be written in vectorial form, making use of a nine-dimensional space of vectors $\mathbf{u}''$ whose coordinates are the variables shown on the first line of Table A2.1 and then subdividing this space into the two subspaces:

$$
\mathbf{u}'\left(\frac{v_{ex}}{j}\frac{m_e\omega_p}{q_e}, \quad \frac{v_{ix}}{j}\frac{m_i\Omega_p}{q_i}, \quad v_{ey}\frac{m_e\omega_p}{q_e}, \quad v_{iy}\frac{m_i\Omega_p}{q_i}, \quad jE_z\right)
$$

$$
\mathbf{u}\left(E_x, jE_y, v_{ex}\frac{m_e\omega_p}{q_e\sqrt{\epsilon_e}}, \quad v_{iz}\frac{m_i\Omega_p}{q_i\sqrt{\epsilon_i}}\right)
$$

(3)

The linear system which describes the determinant is

$$
A_1\mathbf{u}' + A_2\mathbf{u} = 0 \quad (4)
$$

$$
A_3\mathbf{u}' + A_4\mathbf{u} = y\mathbf{u} \quad (5)
$$

The symbols A_1, A_2, A_3, A_4 represent the four matrices separated by lines as shown in (2) (after suppressing y in A_4) or in the schematic:

$$
\left(\frac{A_1}{A_2}\bigg|\frac{A_3}{A_4}\right)
$$

Eliminating $\mathbf{u}'$ from Eqs. (4) and (5), we get

$$
(A_4 - A_3A_1^{-1}A_2)\mathbf{u} = y\mathbf{u} \quad (6)
$$

In $\mathbf{u}$ space, y is then the eigenvalue of the matrix $A_4 - A_3A_1^{-1}A_2$. The computation of this matrix gives

$$A_1^{-1} = \begin{bmatrix} \dfrac{1}{1-l^2} & 0 & \dfrac{l}{1-l^2} & 0 & 0 \\[2mm] 0 & \dfrac{1}{1-L^2} & 0 & \dfrac{-L}{1-L^2} & 0 \\[2mm] \dfrac{l}{1-l^2} & 0 & \dfrac{1}{1-l^2} & 0 & 0 \\[2mm] 0 & \dfrac{-L}{1-L^2} & 0 & \dfrac{1}{1-L^2} & 0 \\[2mm] 0 & 0 & 0 & 0 & 1 \end{bmatrix} \quad (7)$$

$$A_1^{-1}A_2 = \begin{bmatrix} \dfrac{p}{1-l^2} & \dfrac{pl}{1-l^2} & \dfrac{t\sqrt{\epsilon_e}}{1-l^2} & 0 \\[2mm] \dfrac{P}{1-L^2} & \dfrac{-PL}{1-L^2} & 0 & \dfrac{-T\sqrt{\epsilon_i}}{1-L^2} \\[2mm] \dfrac{pl}{1-l^2} & \dfrac{p}{1-l^2} & \dfrac{lt\sqrt{\epsilon_e}}{1-l^2} & 0 \\[2mm] \dfrac{-PL}{1-L^2} & \dfrac{P}{1-L^2} & 0 & \dfrac{LT\sqrt{\epsilon_i}}{1-L^2} \\[2mm] 0 & 0 & p\sqrt{\epsilon_e} & P\sqrt{\epsilon_i} \end{bmatrix} \quad (8)$$

$A_3A_1^{-1}A_2 =$

$$\begin{vmatrix} \dfrac{p^2}{1-l^2}+\dfrac{P^2}{1-L^2} & \dfrac{p^2l}{1-l^2}-\dfrac{P^2L}{1-L^2} & \dfrac{pt\sqrt{\epsilon_e}}{1-l^2} & -\dfrac{PT\sqrt{\epsilon_i}}{1-L^2} \\[3mm] \dfrac{p^2l}{1-l^2}-\dfrac{P^2L}{1-L^2} & \dfrac{p^2}{1-l^2}+\dfrac{P^2}{1-L^2} & \dfrac{plt\sqrt{\epsilon_e}}{1-l^2} & \dfrac{PLT\sqrt{\epsilon_i}}{1-L^2} \\[3mm] \dfrac{pt\sqrt{\epsilon_e}}{1-l^2} & \dfrac{plt\sqrt{\epsilon_e}}{1-l^2} & \epsilon_e\left(p^2+\dfrac{t^2}{1-l^2}\right) & pP\sqrt{\epsilon_e\epsilon_i} \\[3mm] -\dfrac{PT\sqrt{\epsilon_i}}{1-L^2} & \dfrac{PLT\sqrt{\epsilon_i}}{1-L^2} & pP\sqrt{\epsilon_e\epsilon_i} & \epsilon_i\left(P^2+\dfrac{T^2}{1-L^2}\right) \end{vmatrix}$$

$$(9)$$

This matrix is symmetric. Since A_4 is obviously symmetric, the difference $A_4 - A_3 A_1^{-1} A_2$ is also. The roots of y are therefore the eigenvalues of a symmetric matrix. They are the solutions of Eq. (10) (page 121).

It is a well-known property of symmetric matrices ([16], p. 174) that the four roots of this equation are real. We could use the dispersion equation in form (10). For example, by setting $t = T = 0$ (longitudinal propagation), we can verify that the left-hand side of this equation breaks down into a product of two second-order determinants. By setting the first of these equal to zero, we obtain Eqs. (3.10) and (3.11). Setting the second equal to zero, we obtain Eq. (4.8). We note, however, that the matrix A_1^{-1} has singularities at $l = 1$ and at $L = 1$. Hence, Eq. (10) cannot be used for a simple discussion of the phenomena in the neighborhood of these two singularities. We then use, in general, the equation from Table 2.2.

In a certain number of cases it is interesting to transform Eq. (A2.10) by multiplying row and column (3) by $1/\sqrt{\epsilon_e}$ and row and column (4) by $1/\sqrt{\epsilon_i}$. The equation in y is given as Eq. (11) (page 121).

The variables connected with the four columns then are

$$E_x, \ jE_y, \ v_{ez}(m_e\omega_p/q_e), \ \text{and} \ v_{iz}(m_i\Omega_p/q_i)$$

$$\begin{vmatrix}
1 - \dfrac{p^2}{1-l^2} - \dfrac{P^2}{1-L^2} - y & -\left(\dfrac{p^2 l}{1-l^2} - \dfrac{P^2 L}{1-L^2}\right) & -\dfrac{pt\sqrt{\epsilon_e}}{1-l^2} & \dfrac{PT\sqrt{\epsilon_i}}{1-L^2} \\[3mm]
-\left(\dfrac{p^2 l}{1-l^2} - \dfrac{P^2 L}{1-L^2}\right) & 1 - \dfrac{p^2}{1-l^2} - \dfrac{P^2}{1-L^2} - y & -\dfrac{plt\sqrt{\epsilon_e}}{1-l^2} & -\dfrac{PLT\sqrt{\epsilon_i}}{1-L^2} \\[3mm]
-\dfrac{pt\sqrt{\epsilon_e}}{1-l^2} & -\dfrac{plt\sqrt{\epsilon_e}}{1-l^2} & \epsilon_e\left(1 - p^2 - \dfrac{l^2}{1-l^2}\right) - y & -pP\sqrt{\epsilon_e\epsilon_i} \\[3mm]
\dfrac{PT\sqrt{\epsilon_i}}{1-L^2} & -\dfrac{PLT\sqrt{\epsilon_i}}{1-L^2} & -pP\sqrt{\epsilon_e\epsilon_i} & \epsilon_i\left(1 - P^2 - \dfrac{T^2}{1-L^2}\right) - y
\end{vmatrix} = 0 \quad (10)$$

$$\begin{vmatrix}
1 - \dfrac{p^2}{1-l^2} - \dfrac{P^2}{1-L^2} - y & -\left(\dfrac{p^2 l}{1-l^2} - \dfrac{P^2 L}{1-L^2}\right) & -\dfrac{pt}{1-l^2} & \dfrac{PT}{1-L^2} \\[3mm]
-\left(\dfrac{p^2 l}{1-l^2} - \dfrac{P^2 L}{1-L^2}\right) & 1 - \dfrac{p^2}{1-l^2} - \dfrac{P^2}{1-L^2} - y & -\dfrac{plt}{1-l^2} & -\dfrac{PLT}{1-L^2} \\[3mm]
-\dfrac{pt}{1-l^2} & -\dfrac{plt}{1-l^2} & 1 - p^2 - \dfrac{l^2}{1-l^2} - \dfrac{y}{\epsilon_e} & -pP \\[3mm]
\dfrac{PT}{1-L^2} & -\dfrac{PLT}{1-L^2} & -pP & 1 - P^2 - \dfrac{T^2}{1-L^2} - \dfrac{y}{\epsilon_i}
\end{vmatrix} = 0 \quad (11)$$

Computation and Discussion of The General Dispersion Equations

A3.1 Expansion of the Determinant in Table 2.2

In order to expand the determinant in Table 2.2, it is convenient to start with an expansion with respect to the powers of ω_T and Ω_T. Applying the computation rules for determinants, we write the general dispersion relation in the form

$$\Delta_T \Delta_L + B + C + D + E = 0 \tag{1}$$

where

$$\Delta_T = \Delta_1^2 + \frac{\omega_L^2 \Omega_L^2}{\omega^4} (y-1)^2 - \frac{\omega_L^2}{\omega^2} \left(y - 1 + \frac{\Omega_p^2}{\omega^2}\right)^2$$
$$- \frac{\Omega_L^2}{\omega^2} \left(y - 1 + \frac{\omega_p^2}{\omega^2}\right)^2 + 2 \frac{\omega_L \Omega_L \omega_p^2 \Omega_p^2}{\omega^6} \tag{2}$$

$$\Delta_L = \left(1 - \frac{y}{\epsilon_e}\right)\left(1 - \frac{y}{\epsilon_i}\right) - x\left(1 - \frac{y}{\epsilon_s}\right) \tag{3}$$

$$B = \frac{\omega_T^2}{\omega^2} \left(\frac{y}{\epsilon_i} - 1 + \frac{\Omega_p^2}{\omega^2}\right) \left[\Delta_1 \left(y - 1 + \frac{\Omega_p^2}{\omega^2}\right)\right.$$
$$\left. - \frac{\Omega_L^2}{\omega^2} (y-1) \left(y - 1 + \frac{\omega_p^2}{\omega^2}\right)\right] \tag{4}$$

$$C = \frac{\Omega_T^2}{\omega^2} \left(\frac{y}{\epsilon_e} - 1 + \frac{\omega_p^2}{\omega^2}\right) \left[\Delta_1 \left(y - 1 + \frac{\omega_p^2}{\omega^2}\right)\right.$$
$$\left. - \frac{\omega_L^2}{\omega^2} (y-1) \left(y - 1 + \frac{\Omega_p^2}{\omega^2}\right)\right] \tag{5}$$

$$D = 2 \frac{\omega_T \Omega_T \omega_p{}^2 \Omega_p{}^2}{\omega^6} \left[-\Delta_1 + (y-1) \frac{\omega_L \Omega_L}{\omega^2} \right] \tag{6}$$

$$E = \frac{\omega_T{}^2 \Omega_T{}^2}{\omega^4} (y-1) \Delta_1 \tag{7}$$

$$\Delta_1 = y - 1 + x \tag{8}$$

The symbol Δ_T represents the determinant of the two transverse modes. In the absence of magnetic fields, it reduces to $\Delta_1{}^2$. The term Δ_L is the determinant for the two longitudinal modes. Equation (1) is entirely symmetric with respect to electrons and ions.

A3.2   Equation in y

Equation (1) is of the fourth degree in y. The term independent of y is

$$(1-x) \left[\left(1 - x - \frac{\omega_b \Omega_b}{\omega^2} \right)^2 - \left(\frac{\omega_b - \Omega_b}{\omega} \right)^2 \right] \tag{9}$$

A3.3   Equation in $u = y - 1$

By setting $u = y - 1$, we simplify the form of the dispersion equation, which is of the fourth degree in u as it is in y. This substitution gives the following coefficients:
coefficient of $u^4 =$

$$\frac{1}{\epsilon_e \epsilon_i} \left(1 - \frac{\omega_L{}^2}{\omega^2} \right) \left(1 - \frac{\Omega_L{}^2}{\omega^2} \right) \tag{10}$$

coefficient of $u^3 =$

$$-\left(1 - \frac{\omega_L{}^2}{\omega^2} \right) \left(1 - \frac{\Omega_L{}^2}{\omega^2} \right) \left[\frac{1}{\epsilon_e} \left(1 - \frac{1}{\epsilon_i} \right) + \frac{1}{\epsilon_i} \left(1 - \frac{1}{\epsilon_e} \right) - \frac{x}{\epsilon_s} \right]$$
$$+ \frac{2x}{\epsilon_e \epsilon_i} \left(1 - \frac{\omega_L \Omega_L}{\omega^2} \right) + \frac{1}{\epsilon_i} \frac{\omega_T{}^2}{\omega^2} \left(1 - \frac{\Omega_L{}^2}{\omega^2} \right) + \frac{1}{\epsilon_e} \frac{\Omega_T{}^2}{\omega^2} \left(1 - \frac{\omega_L{}^2}{\omega^2} \right) \tag{11}$$

coefficient of u^2 =

$$\left(1 - \frac{\omega_L{}^2}{\omega^2}\right)\left(1 - \frac{\Omega_L{}^2}{\omega^2}\right)\left[\left(1 - \frac{1}{\epsilon_e}\right)\left(1 - \frac{1}{\epsilon_i}\right) - x\left(1 - \frac{1}{\epsilon_s}\right)\right]$$

$$- 2x\left(1 - \frac{\omega_L\Omega_L}{\omega^2}\right)\left[\frac{1}{\epsilon_e}\left(1 - \frac{1}{\epsilon_i}\right) + \frac{1}{\epsilon_i}\left(1 - \frac{1}{\epsilon_e}\right) - \frac{x}{\epsilon_s}\right]$$

$$+ \frac{x^2}{\epsilon_e\epsilon_i} + (x + 1)\left(\frac{1}{\epsilon_i}\frac{\omega_T{}^2}{\omega^2} + \frac{1}{\epsilon_e}\frac{\Omega_T{}^2}{\omega^2}\right) \tag{12}$$

$$+ x\left(1 + \frac{1}{\epsilon_s}\right)\left(1 - \frac{\omega_L\Omega_L}{\omega^2}\right)\frac{\omega_T\Omega_T}{\omega^2} - \frac{\omega_T{}^2 + \Omega_T{}^2}{\omega^2}$$

$$+ \frac{\omega_L\Omega_L\omega_T\Omega_T}{\omega^4}\left(2 - \frac{1}{\epsilon_e} - \frac{1}{\epsilon_i}\right) + \frac{\omega_T{}^2\Omega_T{}^2}{\omega^4}$$

coefficient of u =

$$2x\left(1 - \frac{\omega_L\Omega_L}{\omega^2}\right)\left[\left(1 - \frac{1}{\epsilon_e}\right)\left(1 - \frac{1}{\epsilon_i}\right) - x\left(1 - \frac{1}{\epsilon_s}\right)\right]$$

$$- x^2\left[\frac{1}{\epsilon_e}\left(1 - \frac{1}{\epsilon_i}\right) + \frac{1}{\epsilon_i}\left(1 - \frac{1}{\epsilon_e}\right) - \frac{x}{\epsilon_s}\right] + x^2\frac{\omega_T\Omega_T}{\omega^2}\left(1 + \frac{1}{\epsilon_s}\right) \tag{13}$$

$$+ x\left(\frac{1}{\epsilon_i}\frac{\omega_T{}^2}{\omega^2} + \frac{1}{\epsilon_e}\frac{\Omega_T{}^2}{\omega^2}\right) - x\left(1 - \frac{1}{\epsilon_s}\right)\left(1 - \frac{\omega_L\Omega_L}{\omega^2}\right)\frac{\omega_T\Omega_T}{\omega^2}$$

$$- x\frac{\omega_T{}^2 + \Omega_T{}^2}{\omega^2} + x\frac{\omega_T{}^2\Omega_T{}^2}{\omega^4}$$

coefficient of u^0 =

$$x^2\left[\left(1 - \frac{1}{\epsilon_e}\right)\left(1 - \frac{1}{\epsilon_i}\right) - \left(1 - \frac{1}{\epsilon_s}\right)\left(x + \frac{\omega_T\Omega_T}{\omega^2}\right)\right] \tag{14}$$

A3.4   Equation in x

We can order the terms of the dispersion equation in powers of $1/\omega^2$, that is, as a polynomial in the variable x. The equation is of the third degree in x. The computation of the terms leads to the following results:

x^3 term $=$

$$\frac{\omega_L{}^2\Omega_L{}^2}{\omega^4}\frac{x}{\epsilon_s}\,u^3 - \left[\frac{2x}{\epsilon_s} + \frac{\omega_L\Omega_L}{\omega^2}\left(1 - \frac{1}{\epsilon_s}\right) + \frac{\omega_T\Omega_T}{\omega^2}\left(1 + \frac{1}{\epsilon_s}\right)\right]$$

$$\times \frac{\omega_L\Omega_L}{\omega^2}\,xu^2 + \left[\frac{x^2}{\epsilon_s} + 2x\,\frac{\omega_L\Omega_L}{\omega^2}\left(1 - \frac{1}{\epsilon_s}\right)\right. \tag{15}$$

$$+ x\,\frac{\omega_T\Omega_T}{\omega^2}\left(1 + \frac{1}{\epsilon_s}\right) + \frac{\omega_L\Omega_L\omega_T\Omega_T}{\omega^4}\left(1 - \frac{1}{\epsilon_s}\right)$$

$$\left. + \frac{\omega_T{}^2\Omega_T{}^2}{\omega^4}\right]xu - x^2\left(1 - \frac{1}{\epsilon_s}\right)\left(x + \frac{\omega_T\Omega_T}{\omega^2}\right)$$

x^2 term $=$

$$\frac{1}{\epsilon_e\epsilon_i}\frac{\omega_L{}^2\Omega_L{}^2}{\omega^4}\,u^4 - \left\{\frac{x}{\epsilon_s}\frac{\omega_L{}^2 + \Omega_L{}^2}{\omega^2} + \frac{2x}{\epsilon_e\epsilon_i}\frac{\omega_L\Omega_L}{\omega^2} + \frac{\omega_L{}^2\Omega_L{}^2}{\omega^2}\right.$$

$$\times \left[\frac{1}{\epsilon_e}\left(1 - \frac{1}{\epsilon_i}\right) + \frac{1}{\epsilon_i}\left(1 - \frac{1}{\epsilon_e}\right)\right] + \frac{\omega_L\Omega_L\omega_T\Omega_T}{\omega^4}\left(\frac{1}{\epsilon_e} + \frac{1}{\epsilon_i}\right)\right\}u^3$$

$$+ \left\{x^2\left(\frac{2}{\epsilon_s} + \frac{1}{\epsilon_e\epsilon_i}\right) + 2x\,\frac{\omega_L\Omega_L}{\omega^2}\left[\frac{1}{\epsilon_e}\left(1 - \frac{1}{\epsilon_i}\right)\right.\right.$$

$$\left. + \frac{1}{\epsilon_i}\left(1 - \frac{1}{\epsilon_e}\right)\right] + x\,\frac{\omega_L{}^2 + \Omega_L{}^2}{\omega^2}\left(1 - \frac{1}{\epsilon_s}\right) + \frac{\omega_L{}^2\Omega_L{}^2}{\omega^4}$$

$$\times\left(1 - \frac{1}{\epsilon_e}\right)\left(1 - \frac{1}{\epsilon_i}\right) + x\left(\frac{1}{\epsilon_i}\frac{\omega_T{}^2}{\omega^2} + \frac{1}{\epsilon_e}\frac{\Omega_T{}^2}{\omega^2}\right) + x\,\frac{\omega_T\Omega_T}{\omega^2} \tag{16}$$

$$\times\left(1 + \frac{1}{\epsilon_s}\right) + \frac{\omega_L\Omega_L\omega_T\Omega_T}{\omega^4}\left(2 - \frac{1}{\epsilon_e} - \frac{1}{\epsilon_i}\right) + \frac{\omega_T{}^2\Omega_T{}^2}{\omega^4}\right\}u^2$$

$$- \left\{2x\left(1 - \frac{1}{\epsilon_s}\right) + x\left[\frac{1}{\epsilon_e}\left(1 - \frac{1}{\epsilon_i}\right) + \frac{1}{\epsilon_i}\left(1 - \frac{1}{\epsilon_e}\right)\right]\right.$$

$$+ 2\,\frac{\omega_L\Omega_L}{\omega^2}\left(1 - \frac{1}{\epsilon_e}\right)\left(1 - \frac{1}{\epsilon_i}\right) - \left(\frac{1}{\epsilon_i}\frac{\omega_T{}^2}{\omega^2} + \frac{1}{\epsilon_e}\frac{\Omega_T{}^2}{\omega^2}\right)$$

$$\left. + \frac{\omega_T\Omega_T}{\omega^2}\left(1 - \frac{1}{\epsilon_s}\right) + \frac{\omega_T{}^2 + \Omega_T{}^2}{\omega^2}\right\}xu$$

$$+ x^2\left(1 - \frac{1}{\epsilon_e}\right)\left(1 - \frac{1}{\epsilon_i}\right)$$

x term =

$$-\frac{1}{\epsilon_e \epsilon_i} \frac{\omega_L{}^2 + \Omega_L{}^2}{\omega^2} u^4 + \left\{ x \left(\frac{1}{\epsilon_s} + \frac{2}{\epsilon_e \epsilon_i} \right) + \frac{\omega_L{}^2 + \Omega_L{}^2}{\omega^2} \right.$$

$$\times \left[\frac{1}{\epsilon_e} \left(1 - \frac{1}{\epsilon_i} \right) + \frac{1}{\epsilon_i} \left(1 - \frac{1}{\epsilon_e} \right) \right] + \frac{1}{\epsilon_i} \frac{\omega_T{}^2}{\omega^2} + \left. \frac{1}{\epsilon_e} \frac{\Omega_T{}^2}{\omega^2} \right\} u^3$$

$$- \left\{ x \left(1 - \frac{1}{\epsilon_s} \right) + 2x \left[\frac{1}{\epsilon_e} \left(1 - \frac{1}{\epsilon_i} \right) + \frac{1}{\epsilon_i} \left(1 - \frac{1}{\epsilon_e} \right) \right] \right. \qquad (17)$$

$$+ \frac{\omega_I{}^2 + \Omega_L{}^2}{\omega^2} \left(1 - \frac{1}{\epsilon_e} \right) \left(1 - \frac{1}{\epsilon_i} \right) - \left(\frac{1}{\epsilon_i} \frac{\omega_T{}^2}{\omega^2} + \frac{1}{\epsilon_e} \frac{\Omega_T{}^2}{\omega^2} \right)$$

$$+ \left. \frac{\omega_T{}^2 + \Omega_T{}^2}{\omega^2} \right\} u^2 + 2x \left(1 - \frac{1}{\epsilon_e} \right) \left(1 - \frac{1}{\epsilon_i} \right) u$$

x^0 term =

$$u^2 \left(\frac{u + 1}{\epsilon_e} - 1 \right) \left(\frac{u + 1}{\epsilon_i} - 1 \right) \qquad (18)$$

A3.5   Horizontal Asymptotes of the Dispersion Curve

We obtain the horizontal asymptotes of the dispersion curves by finding the roots of the equation in the limit as x goes to infinity. The term in x^3 dominates, and we obtain an equation of third degree in u. Therefore, there are three horizontal asymptotes. The computation is as follows. We set

$$A = \frac{\omega_p{}^2 + \Omega_p{}^2}{\omega_b \Omega_b} \qquad s = \frac{\omega_T \Omega_T}{\omega_L \Omega_L} = \tan^2\theta$$

$$A' = \frac{\omega_p{}^2 + \Omega_p{}^2}{\omega_L \Omega_L} = A \ (1 + s) \qquad (19)$$

By setting the coefficient, Eq. (15), equal to zero, we get the equation

$$\frac{u^3}{\epsilon_s} - \left[\frac{2A'}{\epsilon_s} + 1 - \frac{1}{\epsilon_s} + s\left(1 + \frac{1}{\epsilon_s}\right) \right] u^2$$

$$+ \left[\frac{A'^2}{\epsilon_s} + 2A'\left(1 - \frac{1}{\epsilon_s}\right) + A's\left(1 + \frac{1}{\epsilon_s}\right) \right. \tag{20}$$

$$\left. + s\left(1 - \frac{1}{\epsilon_s}\right) + s^2 \right] u - A'(A' + s)\left(1 - \frac{1}{\epsilon_s}\right) = 0$$

We can solve this equation by writing it in powers of the parameter s:

$$us^2 - (u - A')\left[u\left(1 + \frac{1}{\epsilon_s}\right) - \left(1 - \frac{1}{\epsilon_s}\right) \right] s$$

$$+ (u - A')^2 \left[\frac{u}{\epsilon_s} - \left(1 - \frac{1}{\epsilon_e}\right) \right] = 0 \tag{21}$$

The solutions are

$$s = u - A' \tag{22}$$

$$s = (u - A')\frac{\dfrac{u}{\epsilon_s} - \left(1 - \dfrac{1}{\epsilon_s}\right)}{u} \tag{23}$$

Solving Eqs. (22) and (23) for u, we obtain the three roots of Eq. (20) and the corresponding values for y

$$y_2 = \epsilon_a(1 + s) \tag{24}$$

$$y_{1,3} = \frac{(\epsilon_a + \epsilon_s - 1)(1 + s) + 1}{2}$$

$$+ \frac{\epsilon\sqrt{[(\epsilon_a + \epsilon_s - 1)(1 + s) - 1]^2 - 4(\epsilon_a - 1)(\epsilon_s - 1)(1 + s)}}{2} \tag{25}$$

ϵ is set equal to $+1$ for y_1 and to -1 for y_3.

A3.6   Oblique Asymptote of the Dispersion Curve

The dispersion curve, in general, possesses an oblique asymptote of the form $u = ax + b$. To determine the coefficient a, we null the terms in sixth degree in x and u, so that, from Eqs. (15) and (16),

$$\frac{\omega_L^2 \Omega_L^2}{\omega^4} \frac{x}{\epsilon_s} u^3 + \frac{1}{\epsilon_e \epsilon_i} \frac{\omega_L^2 \Omega_L^2}{\omega^4} u^4 = 0 \qquad (26)$$

from which (if $\omega_L \Omega_L \neq 0$)

$$a = -\epsilon_e \epsilon_i / \epsilon_s \qquad (27)$$

To determine b, we set $u = ax + b$ in all the terms of fifth and sixth degree originating from Eqs. (15), (16), and (17). Substituting the value in Eq. (27) for a eliminates the terms of sixth degree. By setting the fifth degree terms equal to zero, we obtain

$$b = (\epsilon_e + \epsilon_i - \epsilon_s - 1)\left(1 + \frac{\omega_T \Omega_T}{\omega_L \Omega_L}\right) \qquad (28)$$

The equation for the oblique asymptote is thus

$$y = -\frac{\epsilon_e \epsilon_i}{\epsilon_s} x + 1 + (\epsilon_e + \epsilon_i - \epsilon_s - 1)(1 + \tan^2\theta) \qquad (29)$$

A3.7 Solutions Restricted to the Neighborhood of the y Axis

In the neighborhood of the point $I(x = 0, y = 1)$, we obtain a restricted solution by nulling all the terms of the second and third degree in x and u. Starting from Eqs. (15) to (18), we get

$$(u + x)^2 \left(1 - \frac{1}{\epsilon_e}\right)\left(1 - \frac{1}{\epsilon_i}\right)$$
$$- x^3 \left(\frac{\omega_L - \Omega_L}{\omega_0}\right)^2 \left(1 - \frac{1}{\epsilon_e}\right)\left(1 - \frac{1}{\epsilon_i}\right) = 0 \qquad (30)$$

Hence, we obtain Eqs. (6.14) and (6.15). In the neighborhood of the point A, we can set

$$u = \epsilon_e - 1 + a_e x \qquad (31)$$

By substituting this expression in Eqs. (17) and (18) and by setting the coefficient of x equal to zero, we find

$$\frac{a_e}{\epsilon_e} = \frac{1 - 1/\epsilon_s}{\epsilon_e/\epsilon_i - 1} - \frac{\omega_T^2}{\omega_0^2} \qquad (32)$$

Hence, we obtain Eqs. (6.16) and (6.17).

Polarization of The Modes

By applying the rule of minors to the first line of Eq. (A2.11), we obtain

$$\frac{E_x}{a} = \tag{1}$$

$$
\begin{vmatrix}
1 - \dfrac{p^2}{1-l^2} - \dfrac{P^2}{1-L^2} - y & \dfrac{pll}{1-l^2} & \dfrac{PlT}{1-L^2} \\[3ex]
\dfrac{pll}{1-l^2} & 1 - p^2 - \dfrac{l^2}{1-l^2} - \dfrac{y}{\epsilon_e} & -pP \\[3ex]
\dfrac{PLT}{1-L^2} & -pP & 1 - P^2 - \dfrac{T^2}{1-L^2} - \dfrac{y}{\epsilon_i}
\end{vmatrix}
$$

$$\frac{iE_y}{a} = \tag{2}$$

$$
\begin{vmatrix}
\dfrac{p^2 l - P^2 L}{(1-l^2)(1-L^2)} & \dfrac{pll}{1-l^2} & \dfrac{PLT}{1-L^2} \\[3ex]
-\dfrac{pl}{1-l^2} & 1 - p^2 - \dfrac{l^2}{1-l^2} - \dfrac{y}{\epsilon_e} & -pP \\[3ex]
\dfrac{PT}{1-L^2} & -pP & 1 - P^2 - \dfrac{T^2}{1-L^2} - \dfrac{y}{\epsilon_i}
\end{vmatrix}
$$

$$\frac{v_{ez}}{a} \frac{m_e \omega_p}{q_e} = \tag{3}$$

$$\begin{vmatrix} \dfrac{p^2 l - P^2 L}{(1 - l^2)(1 - L^2)} & 1 - \dfrac{p^2}{1 - l^2} - \dfrac{P^2}{1 - L^2} - y & \dfrac{PLT}{1 - L^2} \\[2ex] -\dfrac{pl}{1 - l^2} & \dfrac{pll}{1 - l^2} & -pP \\[2ex] \dfrac{PT}{1 - L^2} & \dfrac{PLT}{1 - L^2} & 1 - P^2 - \dfrac{T^2}{1 - L^2} - \dfrac{y}{\epsilon_i} \end{vmatrix}$$

$$-\frac{v_{iz}}{a} \frac{m_i \Omega_p}{q_i} = \tag{4}$$

$$\begin{vmatrix} \dfrac{p^2 l - P^2 L}{(1 - l^2)(1 - L^2)} & 1 - \dfrac{p^2}{1 - l^2} - \dfrac{P^2}{1 - L^2} - y & \dfrac{pll}{1 - l^2} \\[2ex] -\dfrac{pl}{1 - l^2} & \dfrac{pll}{1 - l^2} & 1 - p^2 - \dfrac{l^2}{1 - l^2} - \dfrac{y}{\epsilon_e} \\[2ex] \dfrac{PT}{1 - L^2} & \dfrac{PLT}{1 - L^2} & -pP \end{vmatrix}$$

where a is an arbitrary coefficient of proportionality which defines the wave amplitude. In addition, Eq. (2.17) enables us to deduce from expressions (3) and (4) the following equation for E_z

$$E_z = j \left(p v_{ez} \frac{m_e \omega_p}{q_e} + P v_{iz} \frac{m_i \Omega_p}{q_i} \right) \tag{5}$$

From this we obtain Eq. (6) (page 131).

$$E_z = ja \begin{vmatrix} \dfrac{p^2l - P^2L}{(1-l^2)(1-L^2)} & 1 - \dfrac{p^2}{1-l^2} - \dfrac{P^2}{1-L^2} - y & \left(\dfrac{pPLT}{1-L^2} - \dfrac{pPlt}{1-l^2}\right) \\[3ex] -\dfrac{pl}{1-l^2} & \dfrac{plt}{1-l^2} & -P\left(1 - \dfrac{t^2}{1-l^2} - \dfrac{y}{\epsilon_e}\right) \\[3ex] \dfrac{PT}{1-L^2} & \dfrac{PLT}{1-L^2} & p\left(1 - \dfrac{T^2}{1-L^2} - \dfrac{y}{\epsilon_i}\right) \end{vmatrix} \qquad (6)$$

Propagation In Cold Plasmas

A5.1 Equation in u

In Eqs. (A3.10) to (A3.14) we set $1/\epsilon_i = 1/\epsilon_e = 1/\epsilon_s = 0$. The u^4 and u^3 terms disappear. There remains a second degree equation in u whose terms are:

u^2 term $=$

$$
\left[(1 - x) \left(1 - \frac{\omega_L{}^2}{\omega^2} \right) \left(1 - \frac{\Omega_L{}^2}{\omega^2} \right) \right.
$$
$$
+ x \left(1 - \frac{\omega_L \Omega_L}{\omega^2} \right) \frac{\omega_T \Omega_T}{\omega^2} - \frac{\omega_T{}^2 + \Omega_T{}^2}{\omega^2} \tag{1}
$$
$$
\left. + 2 \frac{\omega_L \Omega_L \omega_T \Omega_T}{\omega^4} + \frac{\omega_T{}^2 \Omega_T{}^2}{\omega^4} \right] u^2
$$

u term $=$

$$
\left[2x (1 - x) \left(1 - \frac{\omega_L \Omega_L}{\omega^2} \right) + x^2 \frac{\omega_T \Omega_T}{\omega^2} \right.
$$
$$
\left. - x \left(1 - \frac{\omega_L \Omega_L}{\omega^2} \right) \frac{\omega_T \Omega_T}{\omega^2} - x \frac{\omega_T{}^2 + \Omega_T{}^2}{\omega^2} + x \frac{\omega_T{}^2 \Omega_T{}^2}{\omega^4} \right] u \tag{2}
$$

u^0 term $=$

$$
x^2 \left(1 - x - \frac{\omega_T \Omega_T}{\omega^2} \right) \tag{3}
$$

A5.2   Vertical Asymptotes

a. General equations. We obtain the vertical asymptotes by nulling Eq. (1), the coefficient of u^2. By setting, as previously, $s = \tan^2\theta$ and introducing the parameters A and m, we obtain

$$(1 - x)\left[1 - \frac{m + 1/m}{1 + s}\frac{x}{A} + \frac{x^2}{A^2(1 + s)^2}\right]$$

$$+ \left[1 - \frac{x}{A(1 + s)}\right]\frac{x^2 s}{A(1 + s)} - \frac{m + 1/m}{1 + s}\frac{xs}{A} \qquad (4)$$

$$+ \frac{2x^2}{A^2}\frac{s}{(1 + s)^2} + \frac{x^2}{A^2}\frac{s^2}{(1 + s)^2} = 0$$

Multiplying by $(1 + s)^2$ and grouping with respect to powers of s,

$$\left[1 - x\left(1 + \frac{m + 1/m}{A}\right) + x^2\left(\frac{1}{A} + \frac{1}{A^2}\right)\right]s^2$$

$$+ \left[(1 - x)\left(2 - \frac{m + 1/m}{A}x\right)\right.$$

$$\left. - \frac{x}{A}\left(m + \frac{1}{m} - x - \frac{2x}{A} + \frac{x^2}{A}\right)\right]s \qquad (5)$$

$$+ (1 - x)\left(1 - \frac{mx}{A}\right)\left(1 - \frac{x}{mA}\right) = 0$$

One root of this equation is $s = -1$, an inacceptable root. The second is

$$s = -\frac{(1 - x)(1 - mx/A)(1 - x/mA)}{1 - x\left(1 + \dfrac{m + 1/m}{A}\right) + x^2\left(\dfrac{1}{A} + \dfrac{1}{A^2}\right)} \qquad (6)$$

Written as a function of x, Eq. (6) is of third degree. We shall designate the three roots of Eq. (6) in increasing order by x_{I}, x_{II}, and x_{III} and the three corresponding resonance frequencies by ω_{I}, ω_{II}, ω_{III}. By definition, we therefore have

$$x_{\text{I}} \leqslant x_{\text{II}} \leqslant x_{\text{III}}$$

and

$$\omega_{\mathrm{I}} \geqslant \omega_{\mathrm{II}} \geqslant \omega_{\mathrm{III}} \qquad (7)$$

b. Discussion: resonance frequencies for longitudinal, transverse, and oblique propagation. We can write Eq. (6) in the following form

$$(1 - x)\left(1 - \frac{x}{x_e}\right)\left(1 - \frac{x}{x_i}\right) + s\left(1 - \frac{x}{x'_e}\right)\left(1 - \frac{x}{x'_i}\right) = 0 \qquad (8)$$

1. *For longitudinal propagation* its three roots are

$$x = x_0 = 1$$
$$x = x_e = A/m = \omega_0^2/\omega_b^2 \qquad (9)$$
$$x = x_i = mA = \omega_0^2/\Omega_b^2$$

2. *For transverse propagation* one of the roots is infinite; the other two are

$$x'_e, x'_i =$$

$$\frac{\omega_0^2 + \omega_b^2 + \Omega_b^2 + \epsilon\sqrt{\omega_0^4 + 2\omega_0^2(\omega_b - \Omega_b)^2 + (\omega_b^2 - \Omega_b^2)^2}}{2\omega_b\Omega_b(1 + 1/A)} \qquad (10)$$

using the definition $\epsilon = -1$ for x'_e and $\epsilon = +1$ for x'_i. Recalling that $\Omega_p \ll \omega_p$ and $\Omega_b \ll \omega_b$, we can deduce from Eq. (10) an approximate expression for x'_e and x'_i, obtained by neglecting terms of higher order in $1/m$:

$$x'_e = \frac{\Omega_b^2 + \omega_b\Omega_b \dfrac{2\omega_0^2 + \omega_b\Omega_b}{\omega_0^2 + \omega_b^2}}{2\omega_b\Omega_b(1 + 1/A)} \simeq \frac{\omega_0^2 + \omega_b\Omega_b}{(1 + 1/A)(\omega_0^2 + \omega_b^2)} \qquad (11)$$

$$= \frac{\omega_0^2}{\omega_0^2 + \omega_b^2} = \frac{A}{A + m}$$

$$x'_i \simeq \frac{\omega_0^2 + \omega_b^2}{\omega_b\Omega_b(1 + 1/A)} = \frac{A(A + m)}{A + 1} \qquad (12)$$

We can verify by studying the sign of the product

$$(1 - x/x'_e)(1 - x/x'_i)$$

that for $x = x_e$ and $x = x_i$, we have, for any value of A,

$$x'_e < x_e < x'_i < x_i \qquad (13)$$

The behavior of x_e, x_i, x'_e, and x'_i as functions of A are shown in Fig. 8.1.

3. *For propagation in an oblique direction*, we subdivide the area in Fig. 8.1 with the aid of Eq. (8). The curves representing x_{I}, x_{II}, and x_{III} are located in the shaded regions. We note, in addition, that Eq. (8) is quadratic in A, which facilitates a precise numerical study. Writing in powers of A, we obtain

$$
(1 - x)\left(1 + \frac{1}{s}\right) A^2 - \left[\left(m + \frac{1}{m}\right)\left(1 + \frac{1 - x}{s}\right) - x\right] A x \\
+ \left(1 + \frac{1 - x}{s}\right) x^2 = 0 \qquad (14)
$$

In this form, we see that one of the roots of A vanishes as x goes to $1 + s = 1/\cos^2\theta$, from which we deduce the existence of a vertical asymptote at $\omega = \omega_0 \cos \theta$ (Fig. 8.1). In addition, by nulling, in Eq. (14), the group of terms in third degree in A and x, we obtain the limits of the ratio A/x as both A and x approach infinity:

$$
\left(\frac{A}{x}\right)_{\mathrm{II,III}} =
$$

$$
\frac{1 + \dfrac{m + 1/m}{s} \pm \left[\left(1 + \dfrac{m + 1/m}{s}\right)^2 - \dfrac{4}{s}\left(1 + \dfrac{1}{s}\right)\right]^{1/2}}{2(1 + 1/s)} \qquad (15)
$$

When $s \ll m$ (θ not near $\pi/2$), we can, neglecting terms of higher order in $1/m$, obtain the following approximate relations from Eq. (15)

$$
\left(\frac{A}{x}\right)_{\mathrm{II}} \simeq \frac{2m/s}{2(1 + 1/s)} = \frac{m}{1 + s} = m \cos^2 \theta \qquad (16)
$$

$$\left(\frac{A}{x}\right)_{\text{III}} \simeq \frac{1}{s} \cdot \frac{1}{1 + \dfrac{m + 1/m}{s}} \simeq \frac{1}{m} \qquad (17)$$

These two formulas become Eqs. (8.10) and (8.12) at the corresponding frequencies. They define, for any s, the position of the oblique asymptotes in Fig. 8.1.

Finally, we obtain approximate expressions for x_{I} and x_{II} in the transition region between moderately dense and dense plasmas. This region corresponds to the larger root for A in Eq. (14). Since the ratio of the two roots of Eq. (14) is of order m^2 (see Fig. 8.1), the sum of the roots is essentially equal to the larger one. This is equivalent to neglecting $1/m$ with respect to m, and 1 with respect to m/s. Then

$$A = \frac{mx\left(1 + \dfrac{1 - x}{s}\right)}{(1 - x)(1 + 1/s)} \qquad (18)$$

Now solving this equation for x, we obtain

$$x = \frac{1}{2m \cos^2\theta}\left[(A + m) \pm \sqrt{(A + m)^2 - 4Am \cos^2\theta}\right] \qquad (19)$$

from which

$$\frac{1}{x} = \frac{A + m \mp \sqrt{(A + m)^2 - 4Am \cos^2\theta}}{2A} \qquad (20)$$

Equations (8.7) and (8.8) are obtained from Eq. (20) above.

A5.3   Transverse Propagation

We easily verify from the equation in u that when $\omega_L = \Omega_L = 0$, the equation has a root $u = -x$. The other root is therefore

$$u = -\frac{1 - x - \omega_b\Omega_b/\omega^2}{1 - x + x\dfrac{\omega_b\Omega_b}{\omega^2} - \dfrac{\omega_b{}^2 + \Omega_b{}^2}{\omega^2} + \dfrac{\omega_b{}^2\Omega_b{}^2}{\omega^4}} \qquad (21)$$

$$u = -\frac{[1 - x(1 + 1/A)]x}{(1 - x/x'_e)(1 - x/x'_i)} \qquad (22)$$

A5.4 High Frequency Approximation (Appleton-Hartree Equation)

If, in Eqs. (1), (2), and (3), we set $\Omega_p = \Omega_L = \Omega_T = 0$, the equation in u becomes

$$\left[(1 - x)\left(1 - \frac{\omega_L^2}{\omega^2}\right) - \frac{\omega_T^2}{\omega^2} \right] u^2 + 2\left(1 - x - \frac{\omega_T^2}{2\omega^2}\right) ux \\ + x^2(1 - x) = 0 \tag{23}$$

The dispersion curve is of fourth degree in x and y. It has two vertical asymptotes given by

$$(1 - x)\left(1 - \frac{\omega_L^2}{\omega^2}\right) - \frac{\omega_T^2}{\omega^2} = 0 \tag{24}$$

The other two asymptotes are parallel to the x axis. The coefficient of x^3 is independent of u. Grouping the terms of third and fourth degree in Eq. (23), we get

$$x \frac{\omega_L^2}{\omega^2} u^2 - \left(x + \frac{\omega_b^2}{\omega^2}\right) u^2 - 2\left(x + \frac{\omega_T^2}{\omega^2}\right) ux - x^3 \tag{25}$$

Equation (23) can be put in a common form by first writing

$$\left(\frac{x}{u}\right)^2 + 2\left[1 - \frac{1}{2}\frac{\omega_T^2}{\omega^2(1 - x)}\right]\left(\frac{x}{u}\right) \\ + 1 - \frac{\omega_L^2}{\omega^2} - \frac{\omega_T^2}{\omega^2(1 - x)} = 0 \tag{26}$$

and setting

$$T = \frac{\omega_T^2}{2\omega(1 - x)} \tag{27}$$

$$\left(\frac{x}{u}\right)^2 + 2\left(1 - \frac{T}{\omega}\right)\frac{x}{u} + 1 - \frac{\omega_L^2}{\omega^2} - \frac{2T}{\omega} = 0 \tag{28}$$

whose two roots are

$$\frac{x}{u} = -\left(1 - \frac{T}{\omega}\right) \pm \sqrt{\frac{\omega_L{}^2 + T^2}{\omega^2}} \qquad (29)$$

This result can be expressed in the common form, Eq. (8.22), the result of Appleton and Hartree.

References

1. J. L. Delcroix, *Introduction to the Theory of Ionized Gases*, Interscience, New York (1960).
2. L. Spitzer, *Physics of Fully Ionized Gases*, Interscience, New York (1956).
3. J. F. Denisse, "Etude des ondes électromagnétiques dans les plasmas à partir de l'équation de Boltzmann," published in *Théorie des gaz neutres et ionisés*. Ecole de Physique des Houches, Hermann, Paris (1959).
4. B. Mozer and M. Baranger, "Electric field distributions in an ionized gas," I, *Phys. Rev.*, **115**, 521 (1959); "Electric field distributions in an ionized gas," II, *Phys. Rev.*, **118** (3), 626 (1960).
5. J. H. Piddington, "The four possible waves in a magnetoionic medium," *Phil. Mag.*, **47**, 1037 (1955).
6. Van de Hulst, "Interstellar polarization and magnetohydrodynamic waves. Problems of Cosmical Aerodynamics," *Central Air Document Office* (1951), p. 45.
7. A. Banos, Jr., "Magnetohydrodynamic waves in compressible fluids with finite viscosity and heat conductivity," *Electromagnetic Phenomena in Cosmical Physics*, Cambridge Univ. Press, New York (1958), p. 15.
8. H. Alfvén, *Cosmical Electrodynamics*, Oxford Univ. Press, New York (1950).
9. T. S. Cowling, *Magnetohydrodynamics*, Interscience, New York (1957).
10. D. Bohm and E. P. Gross, "Theory of Plasma oscillations. A. Origin of medium-like behavior," *Phys. Rev.*, **75** (12), 1851 (1949); "Theory of plasma oscillations. B. Excitation and damping of oscillations," *Phys. Rev.*, **75** (12), 1864 (1949).
11. L. Landau, "On the vibrations of the electronic plasmas," *J. Phys. U.S.S.R.*, **10**, 25 (1946).
12. W. P. Allis, "Electron plasma oscillations," in *Proceedings of the Symposium on Electronics Waveguides*, Polytechnic Press of the Polytechnic Institute of Brooklyn, New York (1958).
13. M. Felix and M. Vuillemin, *Ondes dans les plasmas*, Groupe de Recherches de l'Association Euratom-C.E.A., May 1960. To be published under the title: *Relations de dispersion dans un plasma relativiste*.
14. G. Bruhat, *Cours de mécanique physique*, Masson, Paris (1934), p. 525.

15. R. F. Post, "Controlled fusion research. An application of the physics of high temperature plasmas," *Rev. Mod. Phys.*, **28**, 338 (1956).

16. A. Angot, *Compléments de mathématiques*, Editions de la Revue d'Optique, 3rd ed., Paris (1957).

17. M. Bayet, *Physique électronique des gaz et des solides*, Masson, Paris (1958).

18. J. L. Delcroix, J. F. Denisse, and J. M. Pihan, "Calculs relatifs aux propagations d'ondes dans les plasmas." Report LP 6, Laboratoire des Hautes Energies, Orsay (1960).

19. P. L. Auer, H. Hurwitz, Jr., and R. D. Miller, "Collective oscillations in a cold plasma," *Phys. of Fluids*, **1** (6), 501 (1958).

20. J. A. Ratcliffe, *The Magneto-ionic Theory and its Applications to the Ionosphere*, Cambridge Univ. Press, New York (1959).

21. L. R. O. Storey, "An investigation of whistling atmospherics," *Phil. Trans.*, **A246**, 113 (1953).

22. G. B. Field, "Radiation by plasma oscillations," *APJ*, **124**, 555 (1956).

23. T. Pradhan, "Plasma oscillations in a steady magnetic field: circularly polarized electromagnetic modes," *Phys. Rev.*, **107**, 1222 (1957).

24. B. N. Gershman, V. L. Ginzburg, and N. G. Denisov, *Usp. Fiz. Nauk.*, **10**, 561 (1957).

25. D. Quemada, "Expressions générales du tenseur de conductivité $\sigma(\omega, k)$ d'un plasma," *Compt. Rend.* (1961).

Index

A

Adiabaticity, *5*,* 50
Alfvén. *See* Polarization; Velocity; Waves
Appleton-Hartree. *See* Dispersion equation

B

Birefringence, 25
Bohm, D., 41
Boltzmann equation, 2

C

Characteristic lengths, of electron waves, 38
of ion waves, 44
Cold plasmas. *See* Dispersion equation; Plasmas; Propagation; Resonance
Compressibility, *49*
Conductivity, 10, *113*
Coupling, 16, 55, 56
Coupling points, *71*, 73

D

Debye length, *38*, 40
Density, plasma, *1*, *26*, *55*, 59
Dielectric tensor, *10*
Discharges, 57
Dispersion curve, 23
Dispersion equation, *10*, 14
    Appleton-Hartree equation, 17, 84, *93*, *137*
    cold plasmas, *84*
    electron waves, *36*
    general, 14, *65*, 117, *121*, 122
    ion waves, *43*
    longitudinal waves, *32*
    singularities, 15, 65, 78
    transverse, *20*
    transverse propagation, *78*

E

Electron, trapping, 42
    wave, 35, *36*
Energy, caloric, 50
    electrical, *49*, 109
    kinetic, 49, 109
    magnetic, *49*, 109, 111

---

*The italic numbers refer to definitions. The notation is explained on pages 17 and 18.

magnetodynamic waves, 53, *109*
potential, *49*, 111
Energy flux, *50*, 52, 54
Equations, conservation of momentum, *4*, 10
motion, *4*
transfer of electrical energy, 50
transfer of magnetic energy, 50

F

Faraday effect, 25, 28
Field, G. B., 51
Frequencies, collision, 5, 115
critical, 25, *94*
gyromagnetic, *3*, 11
plasma, 2
resonance, 22, *68*, 82, *85*, 134

G

Gross, E. P., 41

H

Hall effect, 29

I

Ion. *See* Dispersion equation; Modes of propagation; Oscillations; Waves

L

Landau damping, 42

M

Magnetic pressure, 31

Magnetoacoustic waves. *See* Polarization; Velocity; Waves
Magnetodynamic approximation, 26
Magnetodynamic waves. *See* Polarization; Waves
Maxwell equations, 4
Modes of propagation, 11, *60*, *71*, 92
electron, 67, *71*, 80
extraordinary, 67, *71*, 100
ion, 67, *71*, 108
ordinary, 67, *71*, 80, 108
orthogonality of, 60, 61
See also Propagation; Waves; Orthogonality

O

Ohm's law, 109
Orthogonality, of magnetodynamic waves, 111
of modes, 60, 61
of waves in cold plasmas, 96
Oscillations, electron, *36*
ion, *43*

P

Plasmas, classification of, *55*, 76
cold, 17, *84*, 132
confinement of, 56, 76, 77
Polarization of waves, *6* , 129
Alfvén, 26
cold plasmas, *96*
extraordinary, 21
high frequency, *97*
magnetoacoustic, *106*
magnetodynamic, *103*
oblique Alfvén, *104*
ordinary, 21
transverse, 15, *21*
transverse propagation, *82*

Poynting vector, *50*
Propagation, in cold plasmas, *84*
   longitudinal, 15, *32*, 72, *76*, 80, 134
   quasi-longitudinal, 72
   transverse, 15, *78*, 87, 93, 94, 134, 136
   See also Modes of propagation; Waves
Pseudoresonances, 82, *90*

R

Resonance, 22, *68*
   in cold plasmas, 82, *85*, 134

S

Space charge, 4
   in pseudosonic waves, 47
Speed. *See* Velocity

T

Transport equations. *See* Equations

V

Velocity, Alfvén, *26*, 58
   drift, 28
   group, 8, 38, 39
   magnetoacoustic, *99*
   oblique Alfvén, *99*
   phase, 8, 39
   pseudosonic, 46
   sound, *34*, 58, 107
   thermal, 5

W

Waves, Alfvén, *25*, 72, 99, 102
   electromagnetic, 54
   electron, 35, 36
   extraordinary, 19
   ion, 35, *43*
   longitudinal, 15, *32*, 54
   magnetoacoustic, *99*, 106
   magnetodynamic, 53, *69*, 72, 79, 89, *99*
   oblique Alfvén, 71, *99*, 104
   ordinary, 21
   pseudosonic, *46*
   sound, 40, 53, 54, 99
   transverse, 15, 16, 19
   See also Dispersion equation; Polarization; Propagation
Whistler mode, 95